VALUE ENGINEERING FOR THE PRACTITIONER

J. JERRY KAUFMAN

NORTH CAROLINA STATE UNIVERSITY
COLLEGE OF ENGINEERING

Produced by   North Carolina State University
Engineering Extension Education
University Box 7902
Raleigh, North Carolina 27695-7902
Tel: 919/737-2356
Fax: 919/737-3803

Printed in the United States
Third Edition 1990

VALUE ENGINEERING FOR THE PRACTITIONER

North Carolina State University, Raleigh 27695-7902
J.J. Kaufman Associates, Houston 77066

Library of Congress Catalog Card Number: 89-62777

ISBN 1-56049-000-4

To

my wife, Harriet, and my staff, Jimmie, John, and Arthur, whose prodding, pushing, and patience made this dream a reality.

ACKNOWLEDGEMENTS

We are indebted to Ron Becker of R.F. Becker Associates, Dallas, Texas for his assistance and support in the development of this text; to Ray Blakely, Engineering Manager for Lufkin, a Division of Cooper Industries, for presenting a VE case study; and to Arthur P. Coletta, Vice President, Fairchild Communications and Electronics for presenting a case study using FAST.

I would also like to acknowledge the considerable production assistance provided by North Carolina State University, especially Julie A. Dean for reviewing and formatting the copy and M.E.Cunning for creating the drawings.

TABLE OF CONTENTS

Chapter 1   Introduction to Value Engineering

Chapter 2   The Information Phase

Chapter 3   Function Analysis System Technique

Chapter 4   The Speculative Phase

Chapter 5   The Creative Skills

Chapter 6   The Planning Phase

Chapter 7   Cost Analysis for Value Engineering

Chapter 8   Experience Curves

Chapter 9   The Execution Phase

Chapter 10   The Presentation Phase

Chapter 11   The Implementation Phase

Chapter 12   Managing Value Engineering

Appendix   Answers to Chapter Questions

Endnotes

Chapter 1

AN INTRODUCTION TO VALUE ENGINEERING

OVERVIEW

This course is dedicated to Value Engineering (VE) practitioners, Value managers and executives who are committed to productivity improvements by increasing the value of products and services to the markets and community they serve.

To the practitioners, this course is a step by step "how to" approach to VE. Each phase of the discipline is defined, and a number of techniques are explained providing the Value practitioner a choice of approaches that best fit the problem or opportunity under study.

For the Value manager, an understanding of the Value principles is important to yield the highest returns for the investment of this effective management resource. Management implications drawn from a wide variety of experiences are discussed in the text and on the videotapes.

To the business executive, this course offers insight into the scope and potential benefits derived from a broad spectrum of applications. Value Engineering has been successfully utilized for component cost reduction; the creation of new and improved products; the development of new market opportunities; and for significant productivity and profit improvements in the cost of doing business.

APPROACH AND PURPOSE

The text portion of this program has been organized for use as either a "stand alone" course, or as a supplement to the video series for which it was principally designed. As the practitioner becomes more comfortable with the material presented, he or she can selectively use, or supplement the video and text, structuring it to the particular business or management style preferred.

The purpose of this course is to indoctrinate the practitioner and user in the principles and techniques of Value Engineering. Training occurs with the application of VE techniques on "live" problems or opportunities. It is because Value Engineering has been successfully applied across a broad market spectrum, covering a wide variety of products and services, that the course material focuses on the principles and concepts of the discipline, rather than singling out specific industries. Regardless of where VE is applied, these principles are the same. Since technique and emphasis on certain phases of the discipline vary with the application and expected result, no one example is carried through to its completion. To do so might imply that VE is only effective on that very narrow application. Instead, various simple, common projects are used to emphasize the principles of VE. The practitioner is encouraged to carry the examples through to their conclusions and to practice and "test" the VE techniques offered.

WHAT IS VALUE ENGINEERING?

The analysis of value is used every day by all of us whenever we make a "buy" decision. We could spend from five cents to twenty or more dollars to purchase a pencil. The receiver of information transmitted by the pencil marks could not distinguish the cost of the pencil. Our handwriting would not improve proportionally to its cost. What value factors are, therefore, considered in the purchase selection?

Lighting a cigarette can be performed with a match, a very expensive lighter, or the more popular disposable lighter. What motivates the selection?

The watch, as a time piece, can be purchased for an amount ranging from ten dollars to over ten thousand dollars with the same performance accuracy. In fact, a comparison of the $10 digital watch with a $500 analog display would probably demonstrate that the $10 product can be read with greater accuracy. Yet, an equal viable market exists for both products.

From the manufacturer's viewpoint, the most important Value principle to remember is: Value is determined by the buyer, not the seller; by the user, not the producer. The understanding of this principle by the Japanese was the key ingredient that made Japan a dominant force in the world's manufactured goods market.

As a consumer, how do we make a "buy" decision?

As a producer, what value factors should be considered in creating or modifying products and services?

As a value feature, when is acquisition cost or price dominant and not dominant?

How can we improve the value of goods or services both as a *producer* and a *buyer*?

To understand Value, in context with Value Engineering, the following definition is offered:

> *Value Engineering is an organized effort directed at analyzing the functions of goods and services to achieve those necessary functions and essential characteristics in the most profitable manner.*

The key terms in the definition are:

an organized effort
Value Engineering uses a methodology that was developed for problem solving over 40 years ago.

analyzing and achieving necessary functions
A deliberate effort is required to identify what is being furnished and what the market needs, as opposed to perceived wants. These elements interface engineering and marketing to define the priority requirements from the point of view of the customer and include the target selling price.

essential characteristics
In addition to achieving the product functions, other requirements must be satisfied such as reliability, maintainability and quality.

in the most profitable manner
Cost is determined by generating and evaluating a range of alternatives including new concepts, reconfigurations, eliminating or combining items, and process or procedure changes. This also considers the operation and maintenance of the product over its normal life expectancy -- the cost of ownership. These elements interface engineering with manufacturing.

THE HISTORY OF VALUE ENGINEERING

Value Engineering evolved in World War II, when General Electric, concerned with the difficulties in obtaining critical listed materials, assigned Lawrence D. Miles, an electrical engineer, to the purchasing department. His mission was to find adequate material and component substitutes to manufacture the designs of needed war equipment. In his search Miles found that each material had unique physical properties that could enhance the product if the design were changed to take advantage of those properties. Expanding the concept into components and products, Miles discovered that he could improve the performance of materials, components, and products while reducing their costs by understanding and addressing the intended function of the design. Miles separated function from activity by defining function as "what it must do" and activity as "how it does it." "Value," said Miles, "can therefore be improved by relating function to cost." This is expressed in the following relationship:

$$Value = \frac{Function}{Cost}$$

Miles named this discipline "Value Analysis." When the Navy adapted Miles' techniques, they changed the name to Value Engineering. Since that time there has been some confusion surrounding the use of the terms "Value Engineering" and "Value Analysis." A common federal government usage defines Value Analysis as an "after the fact" activity, directed toward cost reduction, and Value Engineering as a "before the fact" or product development application.

In marketing, Value Analysis is the effort that identifies and isolates the various market characteristics of Value and the price the market is willing to pay to acquire those product features. Value Engineering describes the design and implementation of those value features into the product. The application definition recommended follows.

> **Value Engineering** - A problem or opportunity involving the physical sciences as the principal discipline in its resolution (product oriented).

> **Value Analysis** - A problem or opportunity involving management and administrative systems analysis as the principal discipline in its resolution (people oriented).

However, whichever definition is applied to the Value Approach, the principles and disciplines are the same.

THE CONCEPT OF VALUE (from the Value Engineering viewpoint)

English is the only language that defines the terms "value" and "worth" almost identically and in common usage, interchangeably.

> **Value** - "A fair return or equivalent in goods, services, or money for something exchanged; the monetary worth of something."

> **Worth** - "Monetary value; the value of something measured by the quality or esteem in which it is held."

> Reference: Webster's Collegiate Dictionary

To differentiate between the two, consider "worth" as a personal determination and "value" as a market assessment. As an example, a painting may be "valued at" $50,000 but it may not be "worth it" to you. The principle value elements are classified as:

> 1. Esteem Value: Want

> 2. Exchange Value: Worth

> 3. Utility Value: Need

Each decision to buy or acquire includes one or all of the value elements. However, the Value Index must be reached or the exchange does not occur. The Value Index includes the consideration of functions and the cost to acquire those functions. Function is defined as:

> FUNCTION - The intent or purpose of a product or system, operating in its normally prescribed manner.

Simply put, function is anything that makes an item or system work or sell. Therefore, value can be expressed as:

$$\text{Value} = \frac{(\text{Esteem}) + (\text{Exchange}) + (\text{Utility})}{\text{Cost}}$$

Although Function cannot be quantitatively expressed, the relationship of function to cost and how it effects value is illustrated by the matrix in Figure 1.1.

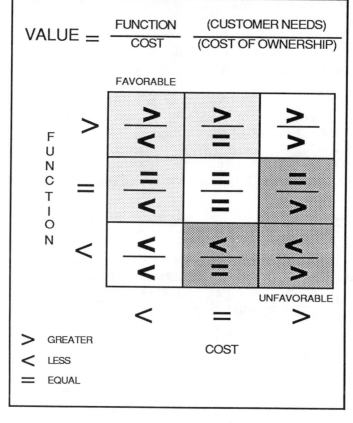

Figure 1.1

From the relationships shown in Figure 1.1, it can be seen that value can be increased by favorably influencing function and/or cost. There are various combinations of influencing value; some are favorable, some are unfavorable. The most desirable relationship is to provide greater function at less cost. (upper left box, Figure 1.1)

When we look at the same item through the eyes of the producer and then through the eyes of the buyer, our sense of value changes.

Value as viewed by the producer:

$$Value = \frac{Function}{Cost}$$

Value as viewed by the buyer:

$$Perceived\ Value = \frac{Perceived\ Benefits}{Price}$$

Regardless of how value is expressed, the dynamics that improve value are the same as those applied to productivity improvement where:

$$Productivity = \frac{Output}{Input}$$

FUNCTION CHARACTERISTICS

When Miles discovered the importance of understanding and analyzing functions, he imposed two principles for identifying and isolating functions.

1. A product or system has many functions which can be divided into broad categories.

   Basic Function - the principle reason for the existence of a "thing."

   Secondary Function - the method selected to carry out the basic function; or those functions supporting the basic function. Secondary functions can be wanted or unwanted.

2. To understand functions, they should be simply expressed using a verb and a noun. Miles found that the number of words it took to describe a function was inversely proportional to understanding the true function.

Combining the two principles, we can describe the following items in function terms:
    chair -- support weight
    screwdriver -- transmit torque
    door -- limit access

Although these examples may appear simple, the function analysis technique is a tedious exercise which must be understood and properly applied. Function analysis is at the very heart of the Value discipline and is discussed in detail in the next chapter.

An incandescent light bulb "illuminates area." However, the incandescent light bulb also produces an unwanted secondary function, "generate heat," because of the method selected to achieve the basic function. Fire would also produce both functions, but "produce heat" may be the basic function in that situation.

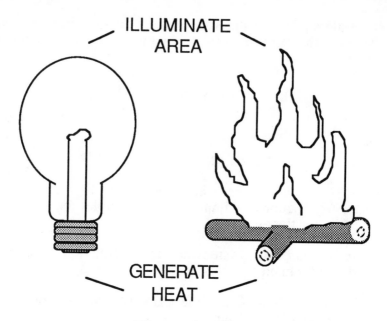

Figure 1.2

Remember, a way to determine if a function is "basic" is to examine the usefulness of the item assuming that function failed. What if a chair could not "support weight," or a screwdriver could not "transmit torque" ("drive screws" is an activity, not a function), or a door could not "limit access"? These examples all have many other desired functions which could be classified as secondary. A product or part could have more than one basic function, but the loss of the basic function(s) causes the loss of the product's (or service's) market value.

LEVEL OF ABSTRACTION

Each small component has a basic function. However, that function may be lost when moving the problem to a higher level of abstraction.

A tie clip's basic function may be described as "restrict movement," but if the analysis involved a suit of clothes, the tie clip's relationship to the suit of clothes would be secondary. A screw's basic function is to "fasten parts," but in a complex product that function may be secondary. Once the basic functions are determined, the search for value involves the cost to perform those functions.

Value Engineering can, therefore, be simply described as the search to find the lowest cost to achieve those necessary functions reliably. "Value" and "bargain" do not relate. A bargain is defined as something you do not need for a price you cannot pass up.

THE VALUE ENGINEERING APPROACH

The two key elements necessary in the search for Value are:

1. The Methodology - a disciplined approach consisting of sequentially structured steps designed to systematically analyze the problem and evolve a creative, cost-effective solution, addressing function.
2. The Task Team - made up of people representing those disciplines necessary to fully define the problem or opportunity and arrive at a cost-effective solution representing the best value. A gathering of a group of people representing various disciplines is a crowd until guided by a structural methodology to mold the "crowd" into a "team."

THE DISCIPLINE APPROACH

The Value methodology consists of sequentially structured steps called the "job plan." The sequence carefully guides the team through problem definition, the creativity process, and through the analytical and presentation phases. The process not only unifies the team, but brings them through the practical application of divergent and convergent thinking.

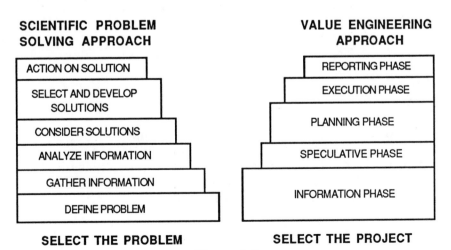

Figure 1.3

Compared to the general scientific problem-solving approach, the VE plan separates the creative process from the other steps in order to encourage the most unique, cost-effective solutions to the assigned project. As such, cost reductions in excess of 30% to 50% are not uncommon. Value Engineers have used different step titles to describe the VE process, dependent on the company and the market it serves. Although the titles are different, the steps are the same. Some of the more common titles are shown below.

"Other" Job Plans

A	B	C	D
Information	Information	Information	Information
Speculation	Speculation	Creativity	Speculation
Planning	Analytical	Evaluation	Evaluation
Execution	Development	Planning	Development
Reporting	Presentation	Reporting	Execution
Implementation	Implementation	Follow-up	

L. D. Miles summarized the pursuit of Value by 5 questions.

1. What is it?
   Describing the project

2. What does it do?
   Identifying its functions

3. What does it cost?
   Allocating cost to function

4. What else will do the job?
   The creative process

5. What does that cost?
   The analysis for "best" value

THE TASK TEAM

The structure of the task team is equal in importance to the VE process in achieving effective results through Value Engineering. There are four major criteria in forming a Value Engineering task team; disciplines represented, level of participation, the number of participants, and competence of participants.

1. Disciplines represented

The project or problem determines the discipline mix charged with the responsibility of resolving that problem. Regardless of the problem itself, be it product, procedures, business, technical, before or after the fact, the team members must represent and be drawn from the following areas: those who are bothered by or "own" the problem; those who are charged with resolving the problem; and those who are effected by the solution to the problem. The third area, often ignored, is significant, because if not adequately addressed, the symptoms of the problem may be resolved only to have the root problem emerge in another area, possibly in another form. As an example, if "cost reduction" is stated as the sole objective, it may be accomplished by adversely affecting customer-desired functions or features. This could result in loss of sales.

2. Level of participation

The problem to be resolved, and its potential impact, determines the level of participants who make up the VE task team. Non-exempt employees should not be assigned problems addressing strategic or business plans. Not only is their knowledge limited, but they may not have a direct vested interest in the results. Conversely, upper management teams should not be formed to resolve component cost reduction problems. Equally important in selecting the level of participants is that team members should be drawn from approximately the same management level. This avoids team dominance by a senior member on the team.

3. The number of participants

Attempting to have every discipline represented on the team could be more detrimental than omitting a few. The span of control for effective task team management ranges from four to seven participants. If additional disciplines are needed, they should be assigned a part-time advisory role, outside the team structure.

4. Competence

Participants should have the competence not only to effectively represent their disciplines, but also to make decisions for their unit or assigned departments without having to continually call their managers for decision confirmation. Consider also that the output solution can be no greater than the proficiency of the team that created the solution.

CLOSING

Subsequent chapters will address each topic discussed in this introduction. Emphasis will be on how to effectively do Value Engineering from a participant and management viewpoint.

As a consumer, the search for value can begin immediately by asking yourself:

1. What functions am I buying?

2. What functions do I really want and need?

3. Is there a more cost-effective way to achieve those functions?

CHAPTER 1 QUESTIONS

1. Who determines the value of products or services offered in the market place?

2. What are the 3 principles characteristics of value?

3. How does Value Engineering differ from conventional cost reduction activities?

Chapter 2

THE INFORMATION PHASE

INTRODUCTION

In the previous chapter the point was made that the difference between a crowd and a team is the structured methodology governing the pursuit of the objectives. This structure is called the "Value Engineering Job Plan." The phases and actions of the VE job plan are outlined below.

Value Engineering Job Plan

Phase	Action
Information	Gather all information on the item. Include specifications and cost data.
Speculation	Brainstorm for alternatives that fulfill or exceed the basic function. Select those ideas with potential.
Planning	Develop "ways and means" for new ideas. Propose methods of measuring cost/time. Advance plans for first, second, third choices.
Execution	Calculate unit and volume costs. Describe feasibility of alternatives. Conduct benefit / risk analysis
Reporting	Present proposals to fulfill function requirements. Highlight all cost and performance gains.
Implementation	Manage project implementation. Report status. Maintain contact with the VE task team.

Although the phases of the VE job plan representing the Value discipline are sequential, the process is iterative. That is, it is often necessary to go back over a previous phase when additional information or issues are uncovered (Figure 2.1). It is acceptable and often necessary to go back, but the team should never skip a step or jump forward.

This chapter covers the first phase of the Value discipline, The Information Phase. There are two distinct parts of the Information Phase, pre-event and post-event. Pre-event is the gathering of information; post-event is the analysis of the information and function determination.

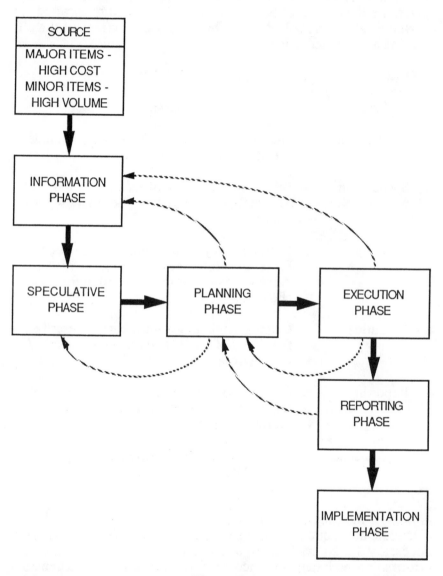

Figure 2.1

PRE-EVENT INFORMATION PHASE

Defining the Problem

As a very first step, the problem must be understood before the information that is valid to the problem can be gathered. This is not as simple as it sounds. Most of us do not know how to define problems. We tend to describe symptoms: "I have a toothache," "my car keeps stalling," "the product or parts costs too much." All are symptoms of larger problems which must be understood and "functionalized" if a VE cost effective solution is to be achieved. As example:

>   toothache   ---- pull tooth vs. fill cavity
>   stalled car   ---- new automobile vs. tune-up
>   product cost -- reduce cost vs. improve profit / sales

Another related characteristic of the problem identifier is called the imposed situation. This is a common situation in which the VE team is told to implement a solution which may not solve the problem or which may result in a poor Value solution for the real problem.

Studying cost effective ways of pulling the tooth is one way to relieve a toothache, but may not be a good Value decision. The pain is gone, but so is the tooth. Reducing the cost of a product may be intended to increase sales; but if the problem of loss of sales is with the inventory and distribution system, cost reduction in not the solution.

A process called *Function Analysis Systems Technique*, which will be described in Chapter 3, is one method of identifying the root problem. Other sources are those found in conventional problem solving techniques (1).

Collecting Information

The gathering of all data and information relative to the task team's principal project, assignment, or objective is the second step of the pre-event information phase. The training of a Value specialist, or facilitator, must also include learning how to seek and collect information. The Value seeker is faced with two conflicting principles representing the spectrum of his investigative process.

>   1. The quality of decisions cannot consistently rise
>   above the quality of information upon which
>   those decisions are made.

2. Considering time constraints, there is never enough information available to the decision maker to make a no risk decision.

These two principles are one important reason for having interdisciplinary task teams perform Value Engineering. The use of a variety of disciplines related to the scope of the problem provides a synergistic opportunity to explore all facets of the problem while focussing on the key issues. As someone once said, "If you organize a task team consisting of seven chemists, I can guarantee that the result will be a chemical solution."

Objectivity

Once the problem is defined, the fact finding process must be objective. Many of us tend to form conscious or unconscious biases and conclusions about the problem from our own personal knowledge and experience. As a result, we tend to disregard information that doesn't fit our preconceived conclusions, and treat as fact those opinions and inferences that do support those conclusions. During the information phase it is not only important to know were and how to seek out valid information, but also to classify that information objectively, i.e., facts, opinions, conclusions, sources of information, etc.

Fact Finding

The scope of the problem will determine the type, amount and sources of information. If, as an example, the problem has been isolated to the cost/function relationship of a product, information will include use, features, sales, and all costs associated with that product. However, if the scope of the problem involves market share, sales, profit margins, business strategies, etc., information must be acquired from these affected sources, and they would be represented on the VE task team. The outline that follows indicates the general kinds of information that should be collected by team members involved in the redesign or modification of a product. Any additional information, data, or examples believed to be helpful in analyses should be included.

THE INFORMATION PHASE -- FACT FINDING

From Marketing/Sales

a. definition of available market served by product offerings and pie-charts in percent and dollars
b. present market goal-product price necessary to achieve sales goals
c. most active competitors -- function/cost comparison (bring competitor's product data, if possible)
d. customer suggestions on features to add/delete from product
e. competitor's weak and strong points
f. product's strengths and weaknesses
g. delivery and distribution effectiveness
h. market voids
i. elements that "drive" the market
j. seasonal considerations
k. image -- service appraisals

From Manufacturing

a. restrictive tolerances of dimensions (difficult to maintain)
b. expensive design specifications
c. high scrap of rework areas
d. current and future capital requirements
e. opportunities for standardizing manufacturing process
f. opportunities for restructuring line flow
g. equipment constraints
h. producibility evaluation
i. cost to produce vs. competition (estimate)
j. availability of resources (labor, material)
k. restrictive government regulations
l. make or buy considerations
m. bottlenecks in the manufacturing process

From Engineering

a. any restrictive product performance specifications
b. unusual environmental or operating requirements, domestic and international
c. administrative or political "roadblocks" or "sacred cows"
d. "back drawer" or "pet" ideas worth exploring
e. detailed drawings, concept sketches, models, photos, hardware
f. technology advances that may affect product offerings
g. new materials applications
h. new product ideas
i. new manufacturing processes

From Purchasing

a. ABC cost break-out
b. single or sole sources - why?
c. high-cost engineering requirements (high receiving - inspection rejects)
d. suggested areas for redesign
e. design features not used in the field

From Quality Assurance/Field Support

a. field failure trends
b. recurring customer complaints/compliments
c. field maintenance problems (MTBR, ease of replacement, etc.)
d. suggested areas of redesign
e. design features not used in field
f. vendor ideas on cost improvement

From Finance

a. standard cost -- labor, burden, material (LBM) of product offerings
b. high cost shop areas
c. high variance cost areas
d. major rework cost centers
e. burden to direct cost ratios
f. trend analysis -- cost-to-price ratios

From General Management

a. business cycles
b. group management concepts, direction
c. facility and capital considerations
d. capabilities and opportunities
e. policy considerations
f. charter

For studies involving hardware, the design reasons for a product are available only from the memories of the cognizant engineers. What history there is of the "why" and "wherefore" for any item is often scattered, and seldom found in one place in comprehensive form. As the value seeker acquires this information, he must write it down. Memory is unreliable because it is influenced by opinions which arise from individual experiences.

Don't underestimate the value of collecting the knowledge and experience of the many people who can contribute technical information on an item. These sources can help define the functions of the item under study. Clarify your understanding of that item and what it is intended to do. Then too, these sources can give you authentic data on what the item does, how and where it is used.

Information must be collected from actual experience. This must include the number of particular items (on a per system basis or per year projection). It must also include customer opinions with regard to the advantages and disadvantages of the item as well as those functions or features valued by the customer. Usable information must concern specific details. Information of a general nature is never satisfactory for a value study.

The following checklist will assist in determining whether the information that has been gathered should be further screened, challenged, or accepted.

Fact Finding Checklist

1. Does the information suggest a redefinition of the problem?

2. Is the information valid for the problem under study?

3. Is the information sufficiently current to be valid?

4. Do the various information items support each other or are they in conflict?

5. If the information is contrary to your initial perception, are the conflicts resolved to your satisfaction?

6. Are there information items that you do not trust as being accurate or representative?

7. Are there relationships or associations between various information items that should be further explored?

8. Do you suspect a behavioral bias in the information?

9. If any information appears to impose a severe restraint on potential solutions, has it been verified by more than one source?

Once the information has been accumulated and digested by the VE task team, the problem must be analyzed to determine those function characteristics describing the problem. Recall the function rules and definitions from Chapter 1, Lesson 1.

1. Use verb and noun.

2. Use active rather than passive verbs.

3. If the function describes performance, try to select measurable nouns. Utility or work functions should be separated from sell functions. One way to make a passive function description more active is to make the noun a verb, then find a more descriptive noun.

Functions*

Passive	Active
Provide support	Support weight
Seek approval	Approve procedures
Develop exhibit	Exhibit product
Submit budget	Budget expenses
Determine resolution	Resolve problems

Passive verbs, such as provide, meet, seek, and all verbs ending in "ize" should be avoided.

Work Functions

Verbs		Nouns	
		Measurable	Non-Measurable
Support	Change	Weight	Component
Transmit	Interrupt	Torque	Device
Hold	Shield	Load	Part
Enclose	Modulate	Light	Article
Collect	Control	Oxidation	Table
Conduct	Attract	Heat	Damage
Insulate	Emit	Flow	Circuit
Protect	Repel	Radiation	Repair
Prevent	Filter	Current	
Amplify	Impede	Voltage	
Rectify	Induce	Energy	

Verbs	*Nouns*	
	Measurable	*Non-Measurable*
Increase	Beauty	Form
Decrease	Appearance	Symmetry
Improve	Convenience	Effect
Create	Style	Loops
Establish	Features	
	Costs	

*Chart courtesy of Dick Dark

If we were to examine a pencil, and identify its components by functions, our findings would be something like the information in Figure 2.2.

DESCRIPTION	FUNCTION	B	S
PENCIL	MAKE MARKS	✔	
ERASER	REMOVE MARKS		✔
BAND	SECURE ERASER		✔
	IMPROVE APPEARANCE		✔
BODY	SUPPORT LEAD		✔
	TRANSMIT FORCE		✔
	ACCOMODATE GRIP		✔
	DISPLAY INFO.		✔
PAINT	PROTECT WOOD		✔
	IMPROVE APPEARANCE		✔
LEAD	MAKE MARKS	✔	

Figure 2.2

Note that the lead in the pencil has the same function as the pencil itself, which is basic. Therefore, all other functions, components, and costs to produce those functions are secondary. However, if the giver of the pencils determines that the pencil is an effective way to advertise his company, the basic function to the giver would not be the same as the user's basic function. Who then determines the value of a product? This may be a philosophical question, but in the final analysis it is still the user, or the buyer, not the giver or producer who determines the value of the products or services. The basic function describes the intended use of the product, not how the product is being used. The pencil can also be used as a door stop, but that is not its intended use.

Note the functions identified with the fuse in Figure 2.3. Which function(s) is basic? Now try to identify at least seven functions of the common products in Figure 2.4 (shoe, filter, tire) and pick out their basic functions.

Functional Analysis

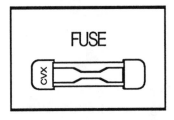

CAN YOU DETERMINE
THE BASIC FUNCTION?

FUNCTIONS	
VERB	**NOUN**
Breaks	Circuit
Connects	Circuit
Protects	User
Protects	Supplier
Warns	User
Protects	Equipment
Identifies	Failure
Advertises	Manufacturer
?	

Figure 2.3

Test Yourself

List Functions - Indicate Basic Function

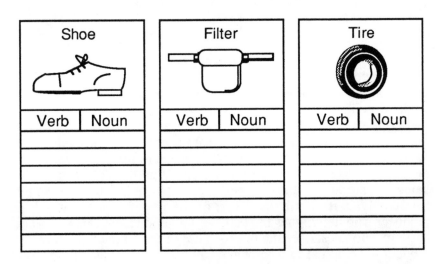

Figure 2.4

There are a number of function analysis techniques. The process called "Random Function Determination" is the most common and is the foundation upon which the other techniques are derived. This process involves randomly dissecting the product or problem and determining if the elements are "BASIC" or "SECONDARY" to the project under analysis. (Refer to Chapter 1 for more information.) There are 4 characteristics to consider in determining if the component should be classified a basic:

Characteristics of a Basic Function

1. Once defined, a basic function cannot be changed.
2. The cost contribution of a basic function is less than 5% of its product cost.
3. You cannot sell basic functions alone, but the supporting (secondary) functions cannot be sold without satisfying the basic function.
4. The loss of the basic function(s) causes the loss of the market worth of the product or services.

COMBINING COST/FUNCTION INFORMATION

Once the components have been identified with their functions and costs, a component-cost-functions matrix can be created. Component cost is then allocated to the functions, and totaled as to the cost and percent contribution to the overall product cost. This quantifies basic and secondary functions and provides the task team with targets of opportunity to make value improvements. Figure 2.5 illustrates what the pencil example (Figure 2.2) would look like in matrix form.

Do not "size" all problems by the pencil example. That is, the analysis of a complex mechanism like an automobile would not be 10,000 times more complex than the pencil. It is the scope of the problem and its level of abstraction that determines its complexity, not the amount of details or the number of component parts. As an example, the illustration of a household wall switch (Figures 2.6 and 2.7) is about 50 times more complex than the pencil. The effort and the time for analysis are about the same. Recalling one of the rules of hardware functions, each component, regardless of how small, has a basic function, particularly when that component is the subject of the study. However, as the problem moves to higher levels of abstraction, the part and its function become proportionately less important.

Function — Pencil

COMPONENTS	COST (CENTS)	REMOVE MARKS %	cost	SECURE ERASER %	cost	IMPROVE APPEARANCE %	cost	MAKE MARKS %	cost	TRANSMIT FORCE %	cost	ACCOMMO-DATE GRIP %	cost	DISPLAY INFO %	cost	SUPPORT LEAD %	cost	PROTECT WOOD %	cost
ERASER	.43	100	.43																
METAL BAND	.25			50	.13	25	.06			25	.06								
LEAD	1.2							100	1.2										
BODY	.94					-0-	-0-			50	.47	-0-	-0-	10	.09	40	.38		
PAINT	.10					50	.05											50	.05
TOTAL	2.92	16	.43	5	.13	4	.11	40	1.2	17	.53	-0-	-0-	3	.09	13	.38	2	.05

Figure 2.5

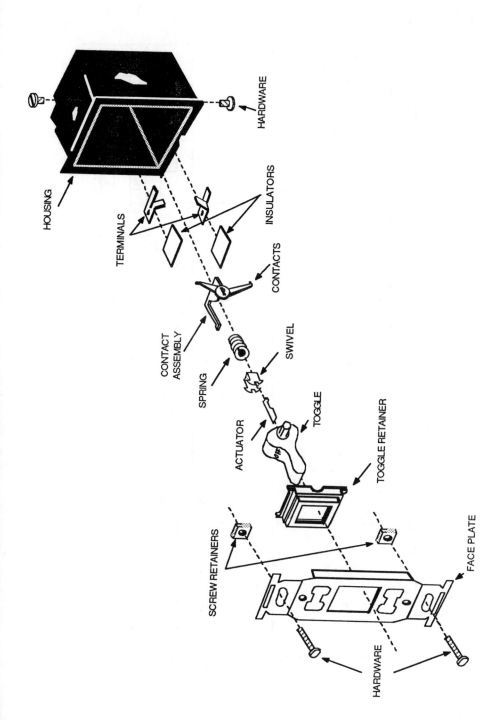

Figure 2.6

2-13

Function

Toggle Switch

COMPONENTS	COST (CENTS)	SUPPORT SWITCH %	cost	TRANSMIT MOTION %	cost	MAKE/BREAK CIRCUIT %	cost	INSULATE CURRENT %	cost	CONDUCT CURRENT %	cost	ENCLOSE COMPONENTS %	cost	ATTACH COMPONENTS %	cost
FACE PLATE	.06	100	.06												
TOGGLE RETAINER	.04	50	.02	50	.02										
TOGGLE	.03			100	.03										
SWIVEL	.02			100	.02										
SPRING	.01					100	.01								
CONTACT ASS'Y	.06					50	.03			50	.03				
INSULATOR	.02							100	.02						
TERMINAL	.04									100	.04				
HOUSING	.04	25	.01									50	.02	25	.01
SCREW	.02													100	.02
TOTAL	.34	26	.09	20	.07	12	.04	6	.02	21	.07	6	.02	9	.03

Figure 2.7

2-14

COST ANALYSIS

Value, as we have discussed, is not absolute; it is relative. The value of anything can only be established through comparative analysis and quantified by analyzing its cost-function relationship. It is, therefore, unnecessary in most VE studies to determine the total cost of all alternatives being considered.

In any product cost comparison there exists certain operations, procedures, assemblies, materials, support, and overhead costs, etc., that are common to each alternative. Since we are looking for the most cost-effective approach, only those non-comparable costs require detailed evaluation to determine the economic difference between alternatives. It is important to note that cost analysis should be treated with as much emphasis as function analysis. The Value Engineer should no more think of guessing at cost than a Design Engineer would guess at a technical approach. Cost could, and should, be tested with the same degree of proficiency as any technical consideration. However, cost analysis, unlike technical analysis, is largely governed by company procedures and will vary among organizations. Cost analysis for Value Engineering will be covered in greater detail in a subsequent chapter.

CLOSING

This lesson has covered the first three of L. D. Miles' five basic questions:

1. What is it?

2. What does it do?

3. What does it cost?

The importance of understanding function cannot be overemphasized. Function analysis is the foundation upon which the Value Engineering Structure is built. The next chapter discusses various function analysis techniques and concentrates on the particularly important approach called *Function Analysis System Technique* (FAST).

1. How does the pre-event Information phase differ from the post-event Information phase?

2. What is the difference between a Basic Function and a Secondary Function?

3. How is a "function" best described?

Chapter 3

FUNCTIONAL ANALYSIS SYSTEM TECHNIQUE
(FAST)

INTRODUCTION

If you accept the premise that understanding the problem is 50% of the solution, then separating the problem from its symptoms and effects by analyzing its function is essential to the process.

The Function Analysis System Technique (FAST) is not an end product or result, but rather a beginning. It lays open the subject under study, forming the basis for a wide variety of subsequent study approaches and analysis techniques.

Developed by Mr. Charles W. Bytheway in 1964, and first presented and published as a paper to the Society of American Value Engineers Conference in 1965, FAST contributed significantly to perhaps the most important phase of Value Engineering - function analysis.

The Value Engineering discipline of describing a function by using a verb and a noun is still intact. Distinguishing between basic and secondary functions and their subsets is also incorporated into the FAST process. The most dramatic differences are in the use of intuitive logic to test the functions and graphic display of them in diagram or model form.

The difference between Random Function Analysis and FAST is that the FAST process looks for the dependence of one function to others. The dependency forms the structure of the FAST model.

Function analysis is a common language, crossing all technologies. It allows multidisciplined team members to contribute equally and communicate with each other while addressing the problem objectively without bias or preconceived conclusions.

As an effective management tool, FAST can be used in any situation that can be described functionally. However, FAST is not a panacea; it is a tool that has limitations which must be understood if it is to be properly and effectively used.

FAST is a system without dimensions; that is, it will display functions in a logical sequence, prioritize them and test their dependency, but it will not tell you how well a function should be performed (specification), when (not time oriented), by whom, or for how much. FAST will not solve problems in the sense that the process will make a solution conspicuously apparent, but it will identify the essential characteristics of a problem, set it up in a logic form and stimulate speculation on how those functions can be implemented.

There is no correct FAST model as in comparing it to some text solution, but there is a valid FAST model. Its degree of validity is directly dependent on the talents of the participating team members and the scope of the related disciplines they can bring to bear on the problem. The single most important output in the multidisciplined team engaged in the FAST exercise is <u>consensus</u>. There can be no minority report. FAST is not complete until the model has the consensus of the participating team members and adequately reflects their inputs.

Although the concept of FAST and the rules for modeling are relatively simple, understanding the process is best achieved by using a hardware example. This will allow the building of a FAST model while applying its principles to something tangible. The product for this purpose will be a spark ignited, gas filled, disposable cigarette lighter.

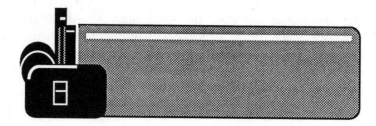

Figure 3.1

There are about 19 individual parts that make up this lighter. Each part, if examined individually, has a basic function, or a principal reason for its existence. However, in evaluating the overall product, not all components are basic to the lighter. To simplify the problem so it doesn't interfere with understanding the FAST process, only the more obvious components will be used.

Using the Random Function Analysis method, we identify the components of the product and determine the functions served by those parts. Then we "randomly" determine if those functions are basic or secondary to the performance of the cigarette lighter in its normal mode of operations.

CIGARETTE LIGHTER
(GAS-FILLED)

COMPONENTS	FUNCTION	B	S
CIGARETTE LIGHTER	PRODUCE HEAT	✓	
BODY	CONTAIN FUEL	✓	
	SUPPORT COMPONENTS		✓
	ADVERTISE PRODUCT		✓
	ACCOMMODATE HAND		✓
VALVE ASSEMBLY	RELEASE FUEL	✓	
	CONTROL FLOW		✓
VALVE LEVER	OPEN VALVE		✓
WHEEL ASSEMBLY	CREATE FRICTION		✓
FLINT	PRODUCE SPARK		✓
	ENERGIZE PARTICLES		✓
SHIELD	PROTECT FLAME		✓

Figure 3.2

In this example the functions "produce heat," "contain fuel," "release fuel," and "generate heat" are considered basic, because if any of those functions fail, the lighter will not perform as intended.

As you probably determined, there can be valid arguments for changing the selection of basic and secondary functions in this example; hence, another reason for the name "random" function analysis. Another shortcoming of the random analysis process is that many operational functions are omitted because the dependency of one function to another is not readily apparent.

A method to identify function dependency, while expanding the number of functions that will be considered in the modeling process, is shown below.

EXPAND FUNCTIONS

WHY	FUNCTION	HOW
Produce Heat	Produce Flame	Ignite Fuel
Transport Fuel	Contain Fuel	Enclosed Fuel
Operate Lighter	Support Components	Assemble Parts
Control Motion	Accommodate Hand	Shape Container
Ignite Fuel	Release Fuel	Open Valve
Manage Flame	Control Flow	Restrict Exit
Release Fuel	Open Valve	Depress Lever
Ignite Fuel	Produce Spark	Rub Materials
Produce Spark	Energize Particles	Strike Flint
Ignite Tobacco	Protect Flame	Control Environment

Note the middle column contains the same functions as in Figure 3.2. Now the questions "how" and "why" are asked. The answers must also be expressed as functions. The HOW and WHY questions are the intuitive logic from the heart of the FAST process. Note the directional reference of the HOW and WHY questions. Test the function dependency by reading across. In the HOW direction, ask "How do you produce heat," by "Producing flame." "How do you produce flame," by "Igniting fuel." Now check the logic by asking WHY across the same line. "Why do you ignite fuel," etc. All other instructions that make up the mechanics of FAST are supplemental to those questions. Two rules should be enforced in the process of expanding the number of functions:

1. Try not to repeat a function that has been identified and posted.

2. Just as in the VE speculation phase, do not prejudge outputs.

The FAST model building process will exclude those functions which are not applicable as well as identify any missing functions. The purpose of this exercise is to get a quantity of related functions while recognizing that not all the functions will fit the final model. Also, the sets of three functions used to test the intuitive logic may be broken up to better fit the FAST model.

To begin the process, a basic model is offered in Figure 3.3 showing the FAST components and describing their parts.

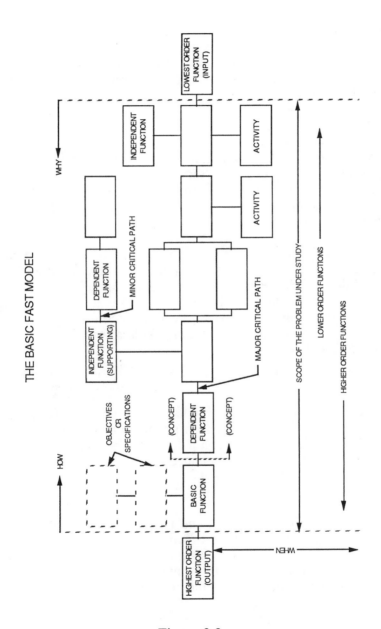

Figure 3.3

A. Scope of the Problem Under Study

Depicted as two vertical dotted lines, the scope lines bound the problem under study, or that aspect of the problem with which the study team is concerned.

B. Highest Order Function(s)

The objective or output of the basic function(s) and subject under study is referred to as the highest order function(s); it appears outside the left scope line and to the left of the basic function(s). Any function to the left of another on the critical path is a "higher" order function.

C. Lowest Order Function(s)

The functions to the right and outside of the right scope line represent the input side that "turn on" or initiate the subject under study and are known as lowest order functions. Any function to the right of another function on the critical path is a "lower" order function.

The terms "higher" or "lower" order functions should not be interpreted as relative importance, but rather the input and output side of the process. As an example, "receiving objectives" could be a lowest order function, with "satisfying those objectives" being the highest order function. How best to accomplish the "satisfy objectives" (highest order function) is therefore the scope of the problem under study.

D. Basic Function(s)

Those function(s) to the immediate right of the left scope line represent the purpose of mission or the subject under study. By definition, basic functions cannot change. Secondary functions can be changed, combined, or eliminated.

E. Concept

All functions to the right of the basic function(s) describe the approach to achieve the basic function(s). The concept represents either the existing conditions (as is) or proposed approach (should be). Which approach to use (current or proposed) is determined by the task team and the nature of the problem under study.

F. Objectives or Specifications

Objectives or specifications are particular parameters or requirements which must be achieved to satisfy the highest order function in its operating environment. Although objectives or specifications are not in themselves functions, they may influence the method selected to best achieve the basic function(s) and satisfy the user's requirements. Note: The use of objectives or specifications in the FAST process is optional.

G. Critical Path Functions

Any function on the HOW or WHY logic is a critical path function. If the function along the WHY direction enters the basic function(s) it is a major critical path, otherwise it will be identified as an independent (supporting) function and be a minor critical path. Supporting functions are usually secondary. They exist to achieve the performance levels specified in the objectives or specifications of the basic functions, or because a particular approach was chosen to implement the basic function(s).

Independent functions (above the critical path) and activities (below the critical path) are the result of satisfying the WHEN question.

H. Dependent Functions

Starting with the first function to the right of the basic function, each successive function is "dependent" on the one to its immediate left, or higher order function, for its existence. That dependency becomes more evident when the HOW question and direction is followed.

I. Independent (or supporting) Function(s)

Independent (or supporting) functions do not depend on another function or method selected to perform that function. Independent functions are located above the critical path function(s) and are considered secondary with respect to the scope, nature, and level of the problem, and its critical path.

J. Function

An end or purpose that a "thing" or activity is intended to perform, expressed in verb-noun form, is a function (refer to Chapters 1 and 2 for function definitions).

K. Activity

The method selected to perform a function (or group of functions) is an activity.

To those who are systems oriented, it would appear that the FAST diagram is constructed backwards, because in systems terms (or WHY direction) the input is normally on the left side and the output to the right. However, note that when a method to perform a function on a critical path is changed, it affects all functions to the right of the changed function. Or stating it in function analysis terms, changing a function will alter all the functions dependent upon it. Therefore, the HOW (reading left to right) and WHY (reading right to left) directions are properly oriented in FAST logic. Another way to look at the HOW/WHY logic is to consider the HOW direction as the function flow and the WHY direction as the system flow. Intuitive logic requires that both directions be satisfied.

STANDARD SYMBOLS AND GRAPHICS

Most examples of FAST diagrams and models show variations in graphically representing the problem. Although the task teams working the exercise understand the notations, it is difficult for outsiders, even those familiar with the FAST technique, to read the model without the aid of a participating team member.

If FAST is to be universally accepted, it must first be universally understood.

The following notations are offered as recommendation for standardizing the symbols and graphics developed after some 300-odd assignments. There have been a number of alternatives in trying to adapt a convention that could be quickly understood, yet allowed graphic flexibility to expand the model when needed. The importance of a graphic standard is in having a common language, not in debating which symbol is used where.

The four (4) primary directions in a FAST model are:

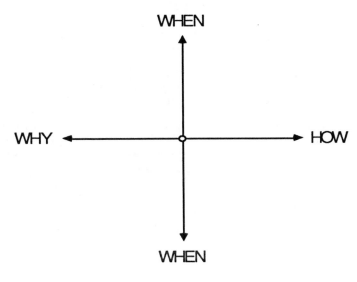

Figure 3.4

The HOW and WHY directions are always along the critical path, whether it be a major or minor critical path. The WHEN direction indicates an independent or supporting function (up) or an activity (down).

At this point, the rule of always reading from the exit direction of a function in question should be underscored so that the three primary questions HOW, WHY, and WHEN are answered in the blocks indicated in Figure 3.5.

1. HOW is (function) to be accomplished? By [B]

2. WHY is it necessary to (function)? So you can [A].

3. WHEN (function) occurs, what else happens? [C] or [D].

The answers to the three questions above are singular, but they can be multiple (AND) or optional (OR). Also, their relative importance can be noted.

INTUITIVE LOGIC

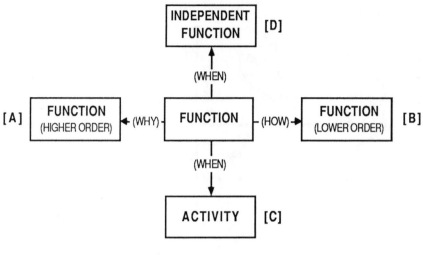

Figure 3.5

ALONG THE CRITICAL PATH - AND

1. "AND" - represented by a split or fork in the critical path.

EXAMPLE A
"AND" (Equally Important)

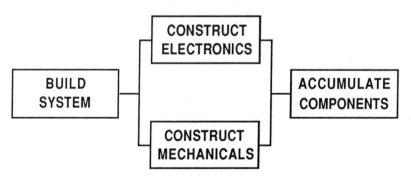

Figure 3.6

In both examples (Figures 3.6 and 3.7) the fork is read as "AND." In Figure 3.6, how do you "build system," by "constructing electronics" AND "constructing mechanicals." In Figure 3.7, how do you "determine compliance deviations," by "analyzing design" AND "reviewing proposals." However, the way the split is drawn, Figure 3.6 shows "constructing electronics" and "constructing mechanicals" equally important; and in Figure 3.7, "analyzing design" is shown as being more important than "review proposals."

EXAMPLE B
"AND" (Less Important)

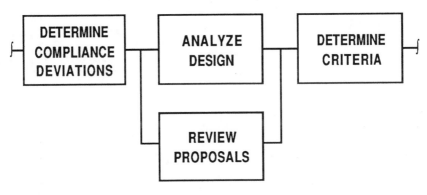

Figure 3.7

2. "OR" - represented by multiple exit lines indicating a choice.

EXAMPLE B
"OR" (Equally Important)

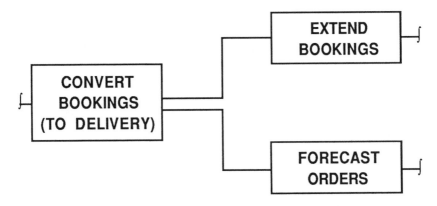

Figure 3.8

EXAMPLE B
"OR" (Less Important)

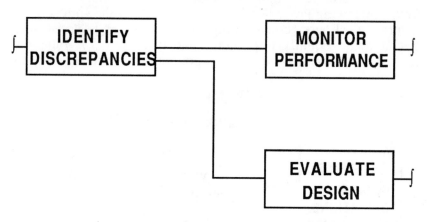

Figure 3.9

Using Figure 3.8, the answer to the question, how do you "convert bookings (to delivery)," is by "extending bookings" OR "forecast orders," not both. When going in the WHY direction one path at a time is followed. Therefore, WHY do you "extend bookings," so you can "convert bookings to the delivery." Why do you "forecast orders," so you can "convert bookings to the delivery."

The same process applies to Figure 3.9, except as in the AND example where "evaluate design" is noted as being less important than "monitor performance."

"AND" - ALONG THE WHEN DIRECTION

For WHEN functions (applicable to independent functions and activities), AND is indicated by connecting boxes above and/or below the critical path functions.

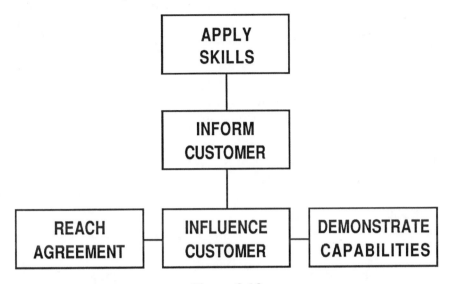

Figure 3.10

The example given in Figure 3.10 states WHEN you "influence the customer" you "inform the customer" AND "apply skills." If it is necessary to rank or prioritize the AND functions, those closest to the critical path function should be most important.

Other notations and symbols used in expressing ideas or thoughts in the FAST model are as follows:

OTHER NOTATIONS AND SYMBOLS

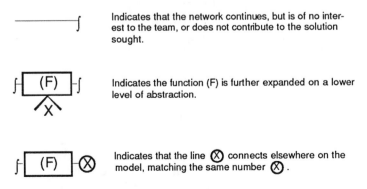

Indicates that the network continues, but is of no interest to the team, or does not contribute to the solution sought.

Indicates the function (F) is further expanded on a lower level of abstraction.

Indicates that the line ⊗ connects elsewhere on the model, matching the same number ⊗ .

Figure 3.11

When the appropriate number of functions have been achieved, or when the team has reached a lull, record the functions individually on precut cards or on 3M's small 1 1/2 x 2 inch "Post-It" note pads. Record just the functions on the cards from all three columns (eliminate duplicates), ignoring the column headings. Next, arrange the functions randomly on a large sheet of paper. Starting with any function, the FAST model can be constructed by linking the functions in the HOW or WHY direction with another. It is best to start with a higher order function, asking "How do you _____?" referring to the function on the note pad. The answer, "by _____," would appear to the right of the first function.

Example: How do you "ignite tobacco," by "producing heat."

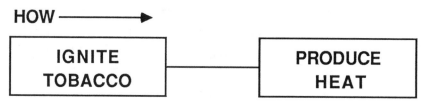

Figure 3.12

Try to select an answer function from among those printed. If a satisfactory answer is missing, add a new card. Continue the process in the HOW direction. How do you "produce heat," by "igniting fuel" and so on.

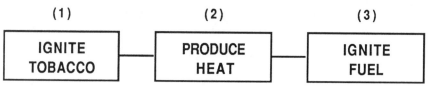

Figure 3.13

The logic should test when asking the WHY question in the opposite direction. WHY do you "ignite fuel," so that you can "produce heat," AND why do you "produce heat," so that you can "ignite tobacco." By continuing to ask the WHY question you will be testing the higher order functions.

EXAMPLE:

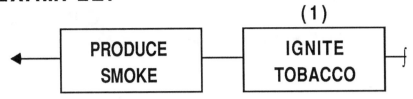

Figure 3.14

Continue in the HOW/WHY direction until the critical paths have been established within the scope of the problem under study. Remember, the critical path can, and often does, split in both the HOW and WHY directions.

Although the FAST model can be developed, starting with any function and building upon it by moving in the HOW (----->) and WHY (<-----) directions, it is recommended that the process start with the highest order function in the HOW direction. Scope lines are placed after the FAST model is developed. Remember, the left scope line identifies the basic function(s).

SUPPORTING FUNCTIONS

Supporting functions appear above and below a function on the critical path and are caused by, or become evident when, that critical path function is active. Support functions are identified by asking the WHEN question.

Some FAST advocates hold to placing support functions that occur all the time above the critical path and those occurring at the same time below the critical path. Others recognize but do not formalize the WHEN direction. A third approach, as recommended here, is to place all independent support functions above the critical path and major activities below the affected critical path function.

FUNCTIONS vs. ACTIVITIES

Since a function and an activity can each be described using a verb and a noun, how do you tell the difference? The definition of a function is "an end or purpose that a 'thing'·or activity is intended to perform." An activity is defined as "the method(s) selected to perform a function." Using an example other than the cigarette lighter, a function is identified as "transmit information;" an activity under that function could be "submit reports."

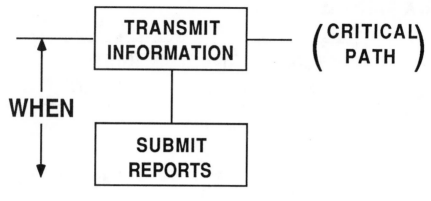

Figure 3.15

Most activities use product or product descriptions as the noun, while the noun in a <u>function</u> is generic. Activities can occur in the HOW or WHY directions of the function. Examples:

Activity	*vs*	*Function*	*vs*	*Activity*
How --->				*<--- Why*
Control <u>Consumption</u>		Restrict <u>Flow</u>		Close <u>Valve</u>
Manage <u>Traffic</u>		Control <u>Access</u>		Open/Close <u>Door</u>
Inform <u>Recipient</u>		Transmit <u>Information</u>		Submit <u>Reports</u>
Create <u>Journal</u>		Record <u>Expenditures</u>		Post <u>Bills</u>
Drive <u>Screw</u>		Transmit <u>Torque</u>		Rotate <u>Shaft</u>
Filter <u>Oil</u>		Trap <u>Particles</u>		Size <u>Opening</u>
Heat/Cool <u>Air</u>		Regulate <u>Temperature</u>		Activate <u>Controls</u>

How do you (VERB) --->

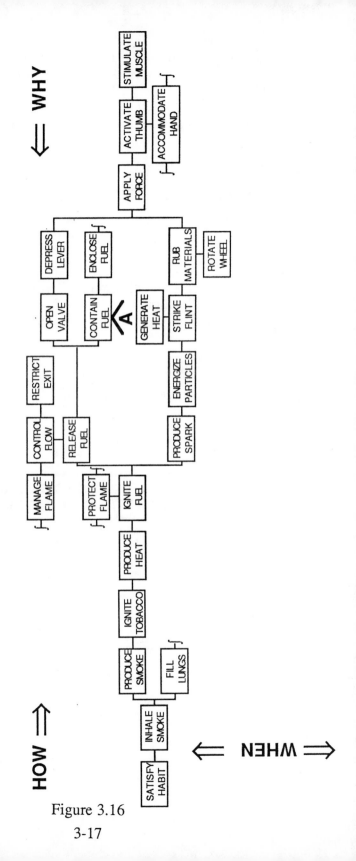

Figure 3.16

3-17

Note that the activity in the Figure 3.17 also satisfies the HOW question, making "submit reports" a function when placed on the critical path.

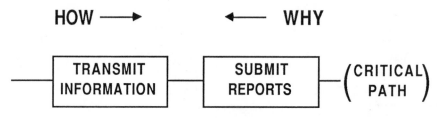

Figure 3.17

To determine if a function should be on a critical path ask the next question, "How do I submit reports?" If that question is leading you in a tangent direction, take it out of the critical path, and test it for an activity (below) or an independent function (above the critical path).

Sometimes expanding a particular function is required in order to facilitate detailed analysis. In the lighter example, if the VE team were interested in the "contain fuel" function they could drop to a lower level of abstraction by isolating and expanding that function, as illustrated.

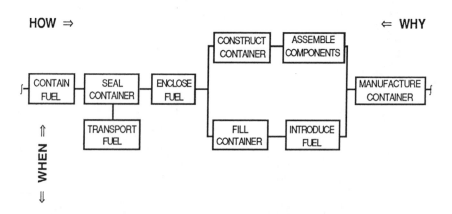

Figure 3.18

However, this example is a controlled move. A major problem occurs in building FAST models when the level of abstraction changes on the same critical path.

Having mastered the answers to the HOW/WHY questions in function form, it is equally important to keep those answers on the same level or plane in which the problem has been expressed. Simply finding an answer that fits the HOW/WHY question is not enough. The answers which are themselves a continuation of the questioning process, within the scope of the problem, must be able to track that problem. As an example, the segment of the engineering drafting function may appear as shown in Figure 3.19.

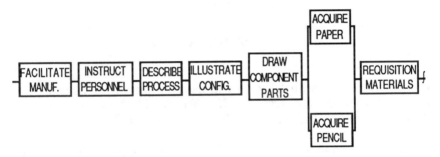

Figure 3.19

Although the answer to the question, "How do you illustrate configuration?" is correctly stated as "draw component parts," the response is on a lower level than the question intended. Continuing in the line of questioning, "How do you draw components?" could bring the response, "By acquiring paper and pencils."

Note the importance of selecting the proper verb. When asking the question "How," you are addressing the verb, i.e., How do I draw _____?, How do I acquire _____? It's the response to the wrong verb that moves the level of abstraction off track. One way to get up to the desired level or track is to express the function "draw component parts" as an activity by moving it in the WHEN direction under the "illustrate configuration" function. Then seek another HOW answer to the "illustrate configuration" question that will satisfy the conditions sought.

LEVEL OF ABSTRACTION

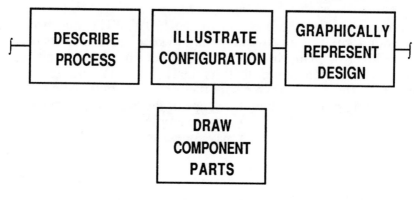

Figure 3.20

Losing the level of abstraction can occur when the critical path is being developed either from the HOW or WHY directions, but lost trails seem to occur most often when following the HOW logic.

Another way to maintain the level of abstraction is to think two or three moves ahead when asking HOW/WHY. Good FAST model builders are like good checker or chess players in this respect; they think ahead of their moves.

An interesting parallel can be drawn by recognizing how similar the "activity" definition is to the "secondary function" definition used in hardware analysis. The approach chosen by the design engineer to implement or carry out a basic function and its resultant product configuration is considered to be a secondary function. Remember, even though a part in a large assembly is secondary to the function of that assembly, the part will have its own basic function if the level of abstraction is lowered and the part itself is the subject of a study. The same logic holds then that an activity can be a function and a function an activity, dependent on the abstraction level of the critical path.

As a general rule, taking activities out of the critical path will raise the level of abstraction of the model. Adding activities to the critical path will lower the level of abstraction.

To start with, the facilitator or study leader should understand the nature of the problem before selecting the team. If the team has already been chosen, the facilitator should advise management of any changes or additions to the team recommended to address the problem fully.

Why a team rather than an individual? Because the problems selected for FAST study are not simple cause-and-effect situations, and a properly constituted team using FAST can bring the most effective and creative solutions to the problem. This is most important in non-hardware, or systems, procedures and organization analysis applications, and when dealing with intangibles.

A guide to choosing the disciplines for the team make-up would be to solicit representation from the "right side" (outside of the right scope line, or lowest order functions), the scope of the problem (between the two scope lines), and the areas effected by the problem (outside of the left scope line, or highest order functions). In analyzing an engineering organization, as an example, consideration should be given to putting a production manager (the output side) on the team, as well as marketing, and sales (the input side), in addition to the engineering representatives (the scope of the problem).

With the team assembled, and before starting FAST, it is important that they agree to the statement of the problem under study because:

A. A common objective, direction, and level is necessary to build and keep the team on the problem rather than on peripheral effects.

B. If properly developed, the higher order and basic functions of the problem are contained within the statements. These can be identified by underlining the verb and noun in the problem descriptions.

Three questions are asked before actually starting the FAST process:

A. <u>What is the problem we are about to discuss</u>? The object of question was discussed above.

B. <u>Why do you consider this a problem</u>? Two purposes are served by asking this question:

   1. The probable causes of the problem are explored as well as prioritizing the need for the solution.

2. The WHY in the question is also a direction (<------). Therefore, by extracting the functions from the answers, the higher order and basic functions selected by the first question can be tested.

C. Why do you believe a solution is necessary? The answer to this question should support, add to, or modify the answer to Question No. 2 as well as output additional functions to explore.

If the problem concerns the restructuring of an organization, the questions should be supplemented with descriptive statements such as the mission, charter, or goals of the unit under study, from which additional functions can be selected.

Hints:

A. Failure to read logically in either the HOW or WHY directions could result from:

1. A missing function which may require a "bridge" function between the two to satisfy the question.

2. An incorrect function or one that moves the critical path to too low or too high a level of abstraction.

3. A function not properly described. This may require using another verb and/or noun to properly identify the function.

It should be emphasized that when asking "how do you _____?," the question addresses the verb, i.e., how do you (pull), (inform), (release), etc. Therefore, selecting the best active verb as well as a descriptive noun is equally important.

B. Develop the major critical path first. The remaining functions and activities can then be appropriately added in the WHEN direction. Building minor critical paths is accomplished by continuing the WHEN functions along the HOW-WHY paths.

C. Leftover functions should be used to build small FAST models, then inserted in the main FAST model.

D. Don't force a conclusion beyond the team's capability to participate and contribute objectively. After a continuous working session (2 to 4 hours), fatigue causes compromises which lead to accepting model entries that are not valid. At this point, it is best to break from the problem for about a half hour. During the break the team should not see or discuss the problem.

When the team reconvenes, go through the HOW and WHY directions from the beginning scope lines, making the appropriate modifications. The breakaway process should be continued as often as necessary to resolve the FAST model.

CLOSING

Practitioners who have been involved in a number of FAST exercises will agree that the dialogue and discussions surfaced in building the model are more important than the model itself. The process of identifying functions, questioning and justifying them, especially by an interdisciplinary team, is key to structuring the problem and moving towards corrective actions. Once the problem has been structured, the model form serves only to explain the team's rationale to outsiders and to communicate across the team disciplines. As important as the model form is, it is a tool to stimulate creative thinking; it is not an end product unto itself.

CHAPTER 3 QUESTIONS

1. What is the difference between an activity and a function?

2. In creating a FAST Model what are the key directional references?

3. What purposes does the scope line serve in the construction of a FAST Model?

Chapter 4

SPECULATIVE PHASE

USING OUR CREATIVITY

Now we come to the Speculative Phase of the Value Engineering job plan. This must be a distinct and separate phase of work, systematically scheduled and timed. It is a challenge to our capacity for creativity.

Compare the phases in a typical, scientific, problem-solving plan with those in the Value Engineering job plan (Figure 1.3). You can see that one difference between the two plans is that the Value Engineering plan considers speculation as a separate phase. (Although speculation is not shown in the typical scientific method, it is used and included in other phases.) To maximize the output, it is best to break this phase out and make it completely separate and readily identifiable. This phase, incidentally, is a period of work that is difficult for anyone to start. Once started, it is difficult to terminate. Our creative ideas have a tendency to snowball once they get in motion.

"Speculate" is a word that most accurately defines this period of contemplation and conjecture. In this phase we start "dreaming up" approaches to the cost-function problem about which we have been gathering information.

IMAGINATION NEEDED

In the information phase functions were identified and named in two-word definitions -- and then you struggled to determine which ones were basic and which were secondary. If you opted to create a function model using Function Analysis System Technique (FAST) you found that identifying and understanding the function relationship of the problem or project was tedious. You wondered why such effort was expended the first time through. Now you find out! You must attack each of the functions separately. Only by speculating on other ways to achieve the critical path functions will you make drastic cost changes. In fact, only in this method of attack can anyone maximize job effectiveness and show significant productivity improvements.

The greatest obstacle in the search for new solutions to problems is the tendency to adopt a "follow-the-past" course. The speculative phase makes us challenge the present. The impulse to speculate is needed in everyone who works on a Value Engineering project.

We have grown to accept as the norm a certain method, design, or material because of habit and the security of familiarization. Yet if a creative environment is encouraged, we venture forth with all kinds of ideas. It has been the imagination of a few that has given us the new products. Many of these are not new inventions in the true sense, but unique applications of existing inventions. They came about by someone's speculating on a function needed.

The very first step to be taken in the speculation phase is to intentionally break with tradition. During the course of our normal working environment, we are sometimes asked for our ideas to solve a particular problem. If the request comes from our social circle, we may joke or present amusing or bizarre proposals. A request from colleagues will usually focus our thoughts on workable, but "safe" or conventional solutions. A request from upper management for ideas will probably cause us to channel our response by trying to anticipate which approaches are wanted and accepted thereby avoiding rejection.

In the speculation phase it is important to remember that the objective is to come up with ideas not solutions. Unlike the "normal" working environment, you are not required to prove or justify the ideas presented. That will come later, during the planning and execution phases and with the support of the other members of your interdisciplinary task team. During speculation judgment is suspended in favor of a free flow of unrestricted, diversified, creative ideas.

Before jumping into the speculation phase, an understanding of our creative traits is important, if the process is to be successful.

CREATIVE TRAITS

Our thinking processes are manipulations of acquired knowledge. It is impossible to have a truly new idea. Rather, we have a metamorphosis of previously acquired information. All the information used to generate an idea was already contained in the intellect at the time the idea was formulated. Although we may not be able to identify the bits of acquired knowledge that were fused to formulate an idea, the information had to be stored in our memory bank somehow, somewhere, at some time. The idea resulted from combining, selecting, distorting, or in some manner manipulating the stored information. Dr. Sidney Parnes likens the mind to a kaleidoscope:

When you look into a kaleidoscope you see a pattern. If you manipulate the drum of the kaleidoscope, you begin to get countless patterns. If you add a new piece of crystal, and hold the drum still, you get a slightly different pattern. Now, if you manipulate the drum, with the new crystal included, you have a multitude of new possible patterns.

The mind operates in a similar way. If you look into the brain, you will find millions of bits of knowledge and experiences stored there -- like information stored in the memory drum of a computer. If you manipulate, "turn on the computer," you get countless patterns -- ideas produced by combination or recombination of existing elements. If you add a new fact or experience, as in adding a new crystal to the kaleidoscope, you add one new pattern. However, as soon as you begin to manipulate, combine, and rearrange the new fact with the old, you get an even greater number of new possible patterns of ideas (2).

Knowledge is the total sum of all that our senses have experienced whether it is acquired in a formal classroom situation or through casually acquired experiences such as viewing a TV program, hearing the sounds of nature, feeling the texture of an animal, or interpersonal reactions with others. We are constantly acquiring new information -- everything we see or hear adds to our knowledge. Much of it is casual information and is rapidly forgotten, such as the everchanging sights observed during an automobile trip. Some of the observed information will be retained for near future recall, such as a highway marker stating there is a dangerous curve ahead. Once the curve is passed the information is forgotten. Periodically, we will witness information that we desire to retain for later recall, such as the roadside antique shop that we would like to visit at some future time. There are different levels of usefulness of information -- immediate, near future, and long term. We generally have a greater awareness of information we intended for recall, and conversely, we tend to have better recall of the information for which we had the greater awareness. If some information impresses us, we are likely to have future recall of it even though there was no definite intent for future need. An increase in awareness of information we receive makes the crystals of knowledge more useful in the metamorphosis of new ideas. The more crystals of knowledge, the more patterns that can be generated by creative manipulation.

The traits covered in this text are those qualities that help us manipulate the crystals of knowledge. It is by virtue of these traits that we are able to link, fuse, separate, distort, invert, and dissect various acquired knowledge to develop new relationships for the solving of problems. Dr. J. R. Guilford, a leading authority on creativity, has identified four primary creative traits:

Problem Sensitivity	=	Awareness of Problems
Fluency	=	Free Flow of Ideas
Flexibility	=	Diversity of Ideas
Originality	=	New Uses or Transformations

PROBLEM SENSITIVITY

Problem sensitivity, an awareness of the existence of a problem, requires a delicate balance. A problem must be perceived before solutions can be developed. However, some people can go through life never seeing problems -- others see problems in everything. Either extreme is counterproductive to problem solving. The problem solver should possess what is commonly termed "constructive discontent."

Problem sensitivity can be aroused by several factors -- it may be an awareness of a conflict of information; it may be an awareness of what is versus what should be. Many of us ignore the existence of a problem because to admit the existence of a problem often requires the responsibility to provide a solution or to determine whether we have a responsibility for a solution. An old and familiar prayer highlights the frustration of problem sensitivity:

> Give me the courage to change those things that should be changed, the strength to accept those things that should not or need not be changed, and the wisdom to distinguish between the two.

The earlier a problem is discovered, the greater the opportunity for more alternatives to a solution. Once a problem has reached the magnitude of a crisis, we tend to be reactive and remove the pressure in any way possible -- generally to alleviate a symptom rather than to solve the problem. An early detection allows us to be more proactive, rather than reactive, in the search for the best solution.

Discovering the problem requires some thinking time -- an endeavor that makes most of us feel guilty. The demands on our time, at work or at home, are such that thinking time is not available. This is often because we are caught up in the vicious cycle of reacting to situations (putting out fires), which prevents us from early discovery or anticipation of problems (fire prevention) resulting in more problems requiring reaction (more fires to put out). It is not long before we become defensive and either deny the problem exists, deny out participation in causing it to exist or persist, or we shift the blame to others. Problem sensitivity will permit early discovery of the problem where the solution can be delegated rather than have the problem reach the magnitude where it can no longer be delegated.

Developing an awareness of problems can be practiced during daily routines. Awareness of problems can be improved by improving our observation and concentration skills. We tend to look but not see, to hear but not listen. How often have we witnessed the same event or heard or read the same things as someone else, only to find that they got more information than we did. Chances are, they were able to observe and concentrate on details, and at the same time, place them in context with a larger overall picture. Developing a habit of seeing what we look at and listening to what we hear in everyday events will strengthen these skills for use in more meaningful situations. As a start toward developing a greater awareness, look at the following exercises.

Figure 4.1

Examine the picture for a moment.

Is the person in the picture male or female? Would you guess by the dress that the weather is warm, mild, or cold? How old would you guess the person is?

If, when you first look at the picture, you can see both the old and young ladies, your "problem sensitivity" is good.

Now try this example. How many "F's" are there in the following statement?

FINISHED FILES ARE THE RESULT
OF YEARS OF SCIENTIFIC STUDY
COMBINED WITH THE EXPERIENCE
OF MANY YEARS.

Did you count 2? 4? Try again.

Now take a moment to describe the illustration in Figure 4.2.

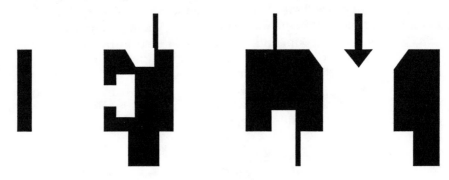

Figure 4.2

Can you make out a word? Try reversing the black and white.

Awareness skills can be directed toward problem sensitivity by developing a questioning attitude about things and events.

How does this (thing) work?
Why was it done that way?
How would I do it differently?
What's wrong with this (thing)?

The next exercise shows you how to apply your observation skills to problem sensitivity and develop constructive discontent.

The following list contains four items that are very familiar. Prepare a list of those things you consider undesirable about each.

What's wrong with:
Dashboard in you car?
Supermarket?
Office desk?
Eating utensils?

As the undesirable features are identified, there is also the tendency to identify ways these undesirable features can be eliminated or minimized. This is the beginning of the problem solving process. Until a problem is perceived, there is no need for a solution.

FLEXIBILITY

Flexibility is the trait that provides nonrigidity in thinking. This trait aids in rejecting habitual, conventional, or previously used ideas, and permits striking out in new directions. Flexibility in thinking permits us to see how solutions or their problems can be used to solve our problems. Eli Whitney utilized this trait when he was trying to invent a mechanical means to remove seeds from cotton.

One day, while struggling with the problem, he noticed a cat trying to catch a chicken through a fence. The cat's claws missed but came away with feathers. From his observation Eli Whitney conceived the solution of pulling the cotton (feathers) through a comb (fence). Previous attempts were directed toward trying to pull the seed out of the cotton. The simple and subtle difference that led to success was to pull the cotton away from the seeds. Whitney's capacity for flexibility was deliberately applied in developing the concept for production of guns. The concept of manufacturing interchangeable parts for the production of guns came from producing multiple quantities of impressions using copperplate engravings.

The opposite of flexibility is rigidity. Most of our experiences reinforce rigidity -- to conform to a social norm; to not question the question; to accept the taught answer as the only answer; to be a "yes man." The following is a list of responses, commonly referred to as roadblocks, that reinforce rigidity and, therefore, inhibit flexibility.

A roadblock is defined as a negative reaction based on an irrelevant assumption supported by unrelated facts.

Ten Sensible Ways to Discourage Innovation

(From Value Management, General Services Administration, Washington, D.C.)

It Isn't In The Budget

Well, maybe it isn't in the budget, but the budget represents yesterday's planning. If reasons are compelling enough, the budget can be -- and should be -- changed. The budget is not a strait jacket intended to freeze all thought and action.

We Don't Have The Time

This is a favorite comment of people who've planned something and don't want their plans changed. If they really want to change things, it's amazing what can be accomplished in a very brief period. How often is there time to delay contract award after bid opening, but never time before bid opening to prevent delay.

Let's Form A Committee

If you're opposed to action, this is a convenient way to put it off. A wise person once defined a committee as a group of unwilling, chosen from the unfit, to do the unnecessary at an unsuitable time.

Has Anyone Else Tried It?

This is a good question -- if it's asked for the purpose of obtaining information. The trouble is that it's so often asked by someone groping desperately for a reason to say no. And a "no" decision solely on this basis is just as wrong as a "yes" decision solely on the basis someone else has tried it.

Why Change It? It's Still Working O.K.

An organization which never changes anything as it works will never be known for progressiveness. Changes that are delayed until they have to be made are often costly and more embarrassing.

We Tried That Before

Did you? Precisely this idea or merely something like it? And how was it executed? Don't be to sure that ideas that were tried and did not work are bad ideas. Many good ideas have failed simply because they were poorly executed.

The Boss Will Never Buy It

How do you know? Did you ask him? How did you ask him? Did you ask him in an off-the-cuff way over lunch or did you present him with a specific, well documented and completely staffed cost savings proposal?

You're Two Years Ahead Of Your Time

Spoken from the vantage point of superior experience, but seldom backed by good sound reasons. This is one of the favorite ways of turning something down without making the person who suggests it feel too badly. After all, who isn't flattered by the thought that he's ahead of his time? The organization, by failing to consider his idea, may find itself behind the times.

Let's Shelve It For The Time Being

A convenient way to kill something without being charged with murder. Those making this remark aren't openly opposed to the idea; they just want to give it time to ripen. What they really want is time for it to die.

It's Against Our Policy

Policies are a valuable guide to action, but there are also times when policy is a poor substitute for good judgment. When a policy blocks progress, it ought to be brought to the attention of people who have authority to change it.

Under proper circumstances, some of the above expressions make sense. That's precisely what makes them so damaging. Wrongly used, they can stop a valuable idea dead in its tracks. When you catch yourself using one of these expressions -- or one like it -- stop and ask yourself a few questions: Do I really mean this? Do I have a good reason for what I am saying or am I merely looking for excuses to kill the idea and avoid reaction? You can't stop progress except in your own department. If an idea is a good one, someone somewhere is going to think of it and put it to use. Why shouldn't it be you? The man who kills progress is killing his own future.

Roadblocks can come from experts who have developed rigidity to the ideas of others. The following statements could have, and perhaps did, set back the development of new ideas.

In 1591 Colonel John Symthe advised the British Privy Council:

> . . . The bow is a simple weapon; firearms are very complicated things which get out of order in many ways . . . a very heavy weapon and tires out soldiers on the march. Whereas, also, a bowman can let off six aimed shots a minute; a musketeer can discharge but one in two minutes.

At a meeting of stockholders of the Western Telegraph Company in 1907, Sir John Wolfe-Barry remarked:

> . . . As far as I can judge, I do not look upon any system of wireless telegraphy as a serious competitor with our cables. Some years ago I said the same thing and nothing has occurred to alter my views.

Sir John Erichsen (1873) commenting on the limitations of surgery:

> There cannot always be fresh fields of conquest by the knife; there must be portions of the human frame that will ever remain sacred from its intrusions, at least in the surgeon's hands. That we have already, if not quite, reached these final limits, there can be little question. The abdomen, the chest, and the brain will be forever shut from intrusion of the wise and humane surgeon.

Even the creative person can develop rigidity to some ideas:

> There is no plea that will justify the use of high-tension and alternating currents, either in a scientific of a commercial sense. They are solely to reduce investment in copper wire and real estate.

U.S. Rear Admiral Clark Woodward (1939):

> . . . As far as sinking a ship with a bomb is concerned, you just can't do it.

and Franklin D. Roosevelt, Assistant Secretary of the Navy (1922):

> The day of the battleship has not passed, and it is highly unlikely that an airplane, or a fleet of them, could ever successfully sink a fleet of Navy vessels under battle conditions.

Admiral William Leahy told President Truman in 1945, concerning the atomic bomb:

> That is the biggest fool thing we have ever done . . . The bomb will never go off, and I speak as an expert in explosives (3).

As a demonstration of flexibility, try the following exercises.

Nine Dots

Without lifting your pencil from the paper, draw four straight connected lines that will go through all nine dots, but through each dot only once.

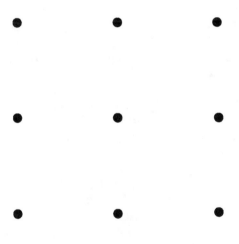

Figure 4.3

Imagine that the six sticks are items of equal length such as matchsticks, toothpicks, or straightened paper clips. The problem is to arrange the sticks to make four equilateral triangles. All ends must touch each other. (All the sides of an equilateral triangle are the same length.)

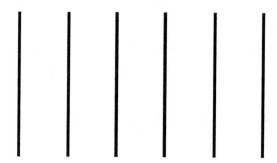

Figure 4.4

In each of these exercises, there is a tendency to impose a rigid constraint on ourselves. In the nine dots exercise, the dot pattern forms a square. We tend to accept the outline of the square as a constraint on the solution. The solution requires going outside this perceived rigid shape. In the four equilateral triangle exercise, the tendency is to try and solve it on a two dimensional tabletop. The six sticks rest conveniently on the flat surface where it is more comfortable to try and arrange them for a solution. The solution requires working in a third dimension to construct a three dimensional pyramid.

These types of exercises serve to illustrate that we unconsciously establish our own constraints. In order to develop flexibility, it is necessary to stretch our thinking. Many of us find it more difficult and uncomfortable to have thoughts beyond the conventional constraints. The more personal and the more practical the problem, the more difficult it is to be flexible. We can solve other people's problems more easily than our own.

FLUENCY OF THINKING

Fluency of thinking permits the generation of a quantity of ideas. This differs from flexibility in that it is concerned with generating a large number of ideas and not necessarily the diversity of ideas. These two traits are highly complementary, but have been identified as distinct traits. It should be stressed that fluency does not exclude flexibility, nor does flexibility exclude fluency. These traits can be likened to the training of an athlete; he learns to be agile and fast. Although separate qualities, they complement each other to the extent that it is difficult to be highly proficient in one and deficient in the other.

Fluency is the trait that helps us overcome the groping for ideas, the searching for words, the struggle to see relationships in things. Most of us have the information stored in memory but have difficulty at times in recall upon demand. Many of us have been conditioned to have recall of one word or one idea and then shut off the recall process. In the fluency trait, we want to keep the recall door open until all the desired information has been retrieved.

ORIGINALITY

Originality is the ability to produce unique ideas. In the context of a creative trait, originality is regarded as uncommon, remote, and clever. An idea can be original to several persons at the same time, or at different points of time. The fact that an idea is statistically infrequent to the originators qualifies it as an original idea. It was stated earlier that new or original ideas were recombinations, or transformations, of previously acquired information. The measure of originality is the degree to which the idea deviates from one that exists -- its uniqueness. Creativity has been defined as bringing something into existence that is unique and relevant. Originality is the uniqueness of the creative act, but is not necessarily usable or relevant in itself.

Originality requires the ability to perceive an item in terms of its functions and attributes, not having a single-minded view of how that item is currently applied. A common bolt, as an example, is used to hold parts together. However, it can be used to separate parts, as in its use as a bearing puller; it can be used as a bumper jack or as a level in leveling pads under household appliances. The threads can be used as a file; the weight can be used as a ballast; the shape can be used to represent various objects in art welding. By giving new meaning to an item, or isolating an attribute of that item, we can transform it into other uses.

A principal reason for forming interdisciplinary task teams in Value Engineering is to stimulate originality. Each participant not only has varied personal experience, but each represents a different professional discipline.

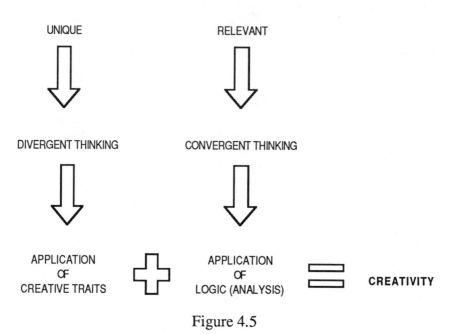

Figure 4.5

BRAINSTORMING

Brainstorming is the best known of all the creativity techniques and has been promoted in many articles. Due to popularity of the term, brainstorming has taken on a more general meaning. The term has come to mean any type of deliberate thinking effort to solve a problem. The technique, as originally developed, is more specific than common usage.

Brainstorming is a deliberate effort to separate divergent thinking and convergent thinking -- to generate ideas without imposing a judgment as to the practicality or usefulness of the idea. The basic principle of brainstorming is that of deferred judgment.

Divergent thinking requires those traits previously described: problem sensitivity, fluency, flexibility, and originality. These are the attributes that stimulate and encourage the development of unique ideas. Convergent thinking requires logic and analysis and encompasses the type of education that we have received in our formal and informal training.

Recent research has added a new dimension. It is now known that we have two interconnecting brain halves, each functioning in a completely different manner. The left brain is used for logical linear thinking. The right brain is used for abstract, spatial, and relationship thinking. For most of us our left brain, which suppresses creative thoughts, dominates because it is better trained and tends to overwhelm the right.

Right Brain	Divergent Thinking	Problem Identification Fact Finding Ideation
Left Brain	Convergent Thinking	Evaluation - Judgment & Selection Development & Implementation

The principle of deferred judgment is valid not only in our own divergent thinking but also in group idea generating sessions. The term brainstorming was originally applied to group sessions when adhering to the principle of deferred judgment. Four rules should be followed.

1. Criticism is ruled out. Judgment is suspended until subsequent evaluation.

2. Freewheeling is welcomed. The wilder the ideas, the better; it is easier to tone down a wild idea than invigorate a tame one.

3. Quantity is wanted. The greater the number of ideas, the more the likelihood of good ones.

4. Combination and improvement are sought. In addition to contributing ideas of their own, task team members should recommend how suggestions of others could be turned into better ideas, or how two or more ideas could be combined into a still better idea. Hitchhike on others' ideas.

These rules, when rigidly enforced by the leader of the brainstorming group, tend to overcome many of the roadblocks to creative thinking. Referring to the list of some typical roadblocks preciously described, it should be appreciated how much freer the ideas will flow when these comments or attitudes are eliminated during an idea generating session.

Dr. Sidney Parnes conducted studies to determine the effect of deferred judgment on the generation of ideas. In his studies, the ideas generated -- the wild ones and the practical ones -- were subsequently screened to pick out the good ideas. His studies showed that people who came up with twice as many ideas in a given time period also came up with twice as many good ideas -- indicating that quantity also breeds quality. Also, 78% of the good ideas were generated during the second half of the allotted time period. Individuals performing solo brainstorming, using the principle of deferred judgment, generated 90 percent more good ideas than individuals not using the principle of deferred judgment. There is a high correlation by different investigators that individuals using the principle of deferred judgment produce significantly more good ideas than individuals not using the principle.

The first step is to specify the brainstorm problem in a manner that will encourage flexibility and fluency. Many problems are stated in such a manner that there is a roadblock present. It may be subtle and unintended, but it is often present. Problem statements such as: How can traffic congestion in cities be reduced? and How can aircraft approach patterns be made safer? have roadblocks. The word "can" implies a possible and practical solution. This word in a brainstorming problem statement becomes a judgment (deferred judgment is wanted) and it tends to restrict the wild ideas. A more open problem statement would be: In what ways might an aircraft approach pattern be made safer? The word "might" instead of "can" is less restrictive and allows the wild ideas to be introduced which may suggest other ideas that are more appropriate to the solution.

Once a diverse group is assembled, it is necessary to create an easy atmosphere in which ideas will flow freely. Participants must feel they are having a good time and feel free to laugh at themselves and at others without any embarrassment. There must be no pressure points. All participants must be peers. You should never mix the vice-president of engineering and an engineer on his staff in the same group. No one should ever feel that somebody is looking over his shoulder.

An atmosphere of free flowing thought must be established. No suggestion is silly. The response of the individuals in the session must be spontaneous with an idea voiced before they have time to reflect and judge the validity or acceptability of an idea. The emphasis should be placed on the volume of ideas rather than on the merit of any particular recommendation. The more suggestions voiced and recorded, the better chance for a successful conclusion. No one should be an expert in the field under consideration. If the problem involves appliances, for example, nobody in the creative session should have made a career in the appliance industry. Experts can tell you why every idea won't work.

Disregard the design description and configuration if a product is being evaluated and stick to its functions. If methods of fastening are being discussed, consider and record all; such as, rivet, bolt, screw, staple, button, zipper, stitch, glue, compress, weld, form, link, strap, tie, tack, etc. Once you have this base of raw ideas to work from, the members of the group will spin off variations in widely diverging patterns. They will add to each other's ideas and create new ones, bringing to bear on the problem a lifetime of knowledge and experience that is unconnected with it.

Remember, you are only concerned with functions at this point, NOT with specific design application. Only after all ideas have been exhausted by the group do you enter the judicial phase of brainstorming. With all ideas prominently displayed, begin to match those applicable specifications and restrictions to the ideas being considered. These restrictions should be considered one by one, starting with those having the greatest effect on the basic function.

Evaluate the ideas for their applicability to each restriction cited. Don't be too hasty in discarding the ideas recorded. Conversely, begin to build and expand on the ideas remaining. Make sure you understand the reason for each specification or restriction.

If no justification can be given, put that restriction aside until a satisfactory explanation is offered or recommend that the specification be waived because it does not contribute to the performance of the product. After all specifications have been considered, use the remaining ideas that stood the test of judgment and proceed with a detailed comparative evaluation to determine a recommended approach.

Brainstorming can be applied to a product in existence or one in the initial development phase. Considering an existing product, the brainstorming approach has developed into a technique called "Blast, Create, and Refine."

The BLAST phase refers to the removal of all sundry functions that are attached to the basic functions of the product. As previously noted, it is a "stripping" process to determine the basic function. During this process we also strip away the justifications that lead to accumulating nonutilitarian secondary functions. These are not discarded, but simply set aside to be reconsidered in turn. The items we are referring to fall in the general classifications of "sales appeal," "appearance," "convenience," and other features. The blasting operation is designed to uncover substantially new areas of investigation, not the nibbling that usually results in minor changes that cheapen the product. We blast to uncover major areas of simplification, substitution, integration, standardization, and especially elimination. To keep a quantitative cost goal in mind, set that goal in excess of a 50 percent reduction -- this is your target, which cannot be accomplished by "nibbling."

Now that we are surrounded by the pieces resulting from the fallout of the blast, we can begin to CREATE. This is the phase formally discussed and related to the "free thinking" process of idea gathering. Remember, all ideas are valid; none are discarded or discouraged. Record everything.

Once this has been accomplished, we can begin to REFINE the ideas to insure functionability, practicability, and reliability. At this point, as previously indicated, we consider the environment, operational conditions, related specifications, and applicable restrictions. We also bring back those secondary function items such as appearance, sales appeal, etc., but view them in their proper perspectives. Also considered in the refinement phase are shape, size, weight, strength, output, life expectance, end use, serviceability, etc.

It is important to keep each of the phases in proper order and not enter into another phase prematurely or mix phases. Although it will be a great temptation to shortcut the process, avoid it. The success of brainstorming depends on this disciplined approach.

Brainstorming a product in the initial development stage is easier to accomplish because lacking the production model, there is no tendency to remain within the configuration of t he product. However, the rewards of accomplishment are difficult to quantify because we don't have the original product to use as a comparison. This does not imply that the actual accomplishments are less. The result of brainstorming a product in its initial development is economically better since the implementation of ideas does not require reinvestments or redesigning the existing product. Regardless of the phase of development to which brainstorming is applied, the success of the technique depends to a large extent on the attitude and dedication of the participants.

Below is a list of questions to stimulate the brainstorming process in the speculation phase.

Idea Needlers or Thought Stimulators

How much of this is the result of custom, tradition, or opinions?

Why does it have this shape?

How would I design it if I had to build it in my home workshop?

What if this were turned inside out? Reversed? Upside down?

What if this were larger? Higher? Wider? Thicker? Lower? Longer?

What else can it be made to do?

Suppose this were left out?

How can it be done piecemeal?

How can it appeal to the senses?

How about extra value?

Can this be multiplied?

What if this were blown up?

What if this were carried to extremes?

How can this be made more compact?

Would this be better symmetrical or asymmetrical?

In what form could this be? Liquid, powder, paste, or solid? Rod, tube, triangle, cube, or sphere?

Can motion be added to it?

Will it be better standing still?

What other layout might be better?

Can cause and effect be reversed? Is one possibly the other?

Should it be put on the other end or in the middle?

Should it slide instead of rotate?

Demonstrate or describe what it isn't.

Has a search been made of the patent literature? Trade journals?

Could a vendor supply this for quicker assembly?

What other materials would do this job?

What is similar to this but costs less? Why?

What if it were made lighter or faster?

What motion or power is wasted?

Could the package be used for something afterwards?

If all specifications could be forgotten, how else could the basic function be accomplished?

Could these be made to meet specifications?

How do competitors solve problems similar to this?

SPECULATION PHASE PROCEDURES SUMMARY

1. Select each basic function and blast or isolate that segment from the remainder of the problem.

2. Addressing just the function, come up with several ideas to achieve that function. There are two important rules to remember:

   a. A basic function cannot change; however, the manner in which that basic function is performed is open to "speculation." As an example, if the basic function is to "produce heat," utilize all of your creative ability to come up with as many ways as possible to "produce heat."

   b. You are looking for ideas, not solutions. Don't judge your or any of your team members' responses.

3. Record all inputs. Again, the temptation to judge and reject ideas will be strong. However, the idea must be presented and visible -- not necessarily for its own contribution, but for other ideas it may generate in the hitchhiking process.

4. Combine and group functions and ideas to stimulate still more ideas in different forms or approaches.

5. Determine how many secondary functions can be reduced, combined, or eliminated by the ideas generated to achieve the basic functions. Remember, each component when analyzed by itself has a basic function, but is that function basic to the product or problem? If the functions are not necessary, neither are the parts that support those functions.

6. Numerically list and categorize the ideas so they can be evaluated later.

CHAPTER 4 QUESTIONS

1. What are the 4 major creativity attributes?

2. What is a "roadblock?"

3. Identify the 4 rules in Brainstorming.

Chapter 5

HEY, ENGINEERS ARE PEOPLE, TOO!
(THE SOFTWARE OF PROJECT ENGINEERING)

Lee Harrisberger
Professor of Mechanical Engineering
University of Alabama

SUMMARY

There is more to engineering practice than analysis and computation. Surveys indicate that at least 60 percent of an engineer's day is spent dealing with people at a broad range of levels of responsibility.

In the ME Design Clinic at The University of Alabama, I have been using a variety of diagnostic instruments to identify a graduate's profile of professional-level, people-managing skills. This report discusses the skills and proficiencies that ME seniors have as they enter engineering practice.

The skills include: Personality Style, Creativity, Leadership, Teammanship (Small Group Management), Conflict Management, Listening, Motivation, and Assertiveness. The data show a consistent profile of personal styles that indicate these graduates must make some changes in their behavior patterns to develop an effective set of career skills.

THE SOFTWARE OF ENGINEERING

Engineering professors who teach design and engineering problem solving have always known there is more to design than analysis. An engineer doing engineering design/problem solving is a detective who must search for all the facts of the case, sort them all out, look for all the alternatives, and find the best "fit" for the circumstances. He always works for a client, must interact with all who are involved, search out people with prior experience and specialized expertise, deal with vendors, salesmen, and entrepreneurs who have the "off-the-shelve" parts, develop some clever ideas for a solution to the dilemma, and then mount a sales promotion to get the financial/managerial decision-makers to accept the proposal. They are constantly communicating -- talking and listening to professional people. They rarely work alone, most commonly work in small teams of peers, and inevitably are involved in the management of people, projects, and information. These activities involve the software of engineering -- the interpersonal skills of dealing with professional level people.

As a prerequisite to entering our ME Clinic Internship Program* all of our ME seniors must take a three-credit-hour Career Readiness Course which focuses on these software skills of engineering practice. The objective is to identify the skill levels and behavioral styles each student possesses. There has been no attempt to train/retrain the student. The intent is to show him the way he prefers to deal with each of the issues and point out which style is most appropriate. If he has a mismatch in his preferred way and the recommended way to handle the situation, he can identify what he needs to do to improve his proficiency. We leave it to him to decide whether to cope with it or avoid it.

There is a long list of personal skills which are employed by engineers on the job. In the Clinic, I selected the skills and attributes which have a high job demand and were measurable by an "off-the-shelf" diagnostic indicator. These "people characteristics" include:

- Personality Style
- Creative Potential
- Listening Skill
- Leadership and Conflict Management Style
- Assertiveness Skill
- Motivational Style
- Teammanship Style
- Non-Verbal Communication Style

The diagnostics are administered and scored in class. Class profiles are prepared so that every student has both a profile of his peer group and a personal record of his own profile. Wherever possible, the information is related to other personal characteristics and job situations. During the various Clinic team activities, debriefing sessions are used to examine individual traits, responses, and attitudes to the identified styles.

Since the Clinic was founded in 1978, I have collected data on four classes of mechanical engineering seniors. Interesting patterns and relationships are emerging which have a remarkable consistency and predictablility. They present some insights into the needs and opportunities for preparing engineering students to enter a career.

---

* The internship involves a 3-credit hour, 3-person team consulting assignment to solve a design problem for an industrial client.

I have found the Myers-Briggs Personality Indicator (MBTI) to be one of the most interesting and useful diagnostics in the set. It is a no-threat positively-oriented, no-jargon, identifier of the basic style of behavior of an individual. It can be completed and self-scored in about 40 minutes. It sparks tremendous individual interest and curiosity and a willingness to learn to observe the differences in people types and behaviors.

The MBTI describes the "hard-wired" basic (genetic) style of behavior as opposed to acquired, experienced-based (software) behaviors. It predicts the pattern (or trajectory) a person will follow when "push-comes-to-shove." The personal characteristics it identifies explain and correlate with many of the other diagnostics used in the Clinic. This happy relationship reinforces the value and usefulness of all the information and adds credibility to its applicability to career demands.

The instrument identifies eight dimensions of behavior on an either/or basis so that everyone is identified by a four letter word, i.e., your personality style is defined as a four-dimensional attribute. The four pairs are:

1. E = externally (people) oriented (extraverted)
   I = internally (thing-concept) oriented (introverted)
2. S = practical, pragmatic, experience and data oriented (sensing)
   N = idealistic, creative, concept and future oriented (intuitive)
3. T = rational, cognitive (left brain) oriented (thinking)
   F = sensitive, emotional, affective (right brain) oriented (feeling)
4. J = organized, outcome oriented, decision maker (judging)
   P = curious, diagnostic, action oriented, researcher (perceptive)

In addition, the diagnostic identifies four temperaments styles which provide predictable insights to personal styles of learning, mating, and people managing. The temperaments are identified by the unusually different styles people use to deal with situations when they possess one of the following pairs of MBTI characteristics:

SJ = dependable, responsible, duty oriented, conservative, workaholic
SP = fun loving, impulsive, participator, investigator
NF = caring, concerned, people-oriented communicator
NT = planner, scholar, designer, loner, intellectual

Figure 5.1 shows the summary profile of the distribution of the eight personality characteristics that occur among the mechanical engineering seniors in the Clinic. This profile is compared to the MBTI engineering school profile of 3030 engineering freshmen collected from a variety of engineering schools. Although there are slight variations in percentages from one class to another, the profile remains consistent. The stereotype personality (over 50 percent in each trait) is ISTJ.

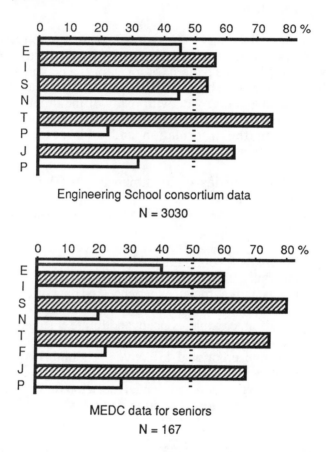

Engineering School consortium data
N = 3030

MEDC data for seniors
N = 167

MBTI type distribution. ME seniors vs.
freshmen consortium data.

Figure 5.1

Figure 5.2 is s a profile of the distribution of the four temperaments among our ME seniors. The preponderance of SJ and NT styles is evident. The type characteristics of SJs explain why they tend to move into plant engineering testing/analysis/operation and management activities. NTs become involved in design, development, consulting, research, advanced degrees, and professorships. The percentage of NTs in the engineering student population correlates with high entrance test scores. NTs consistently obtain higher test scores and grades.

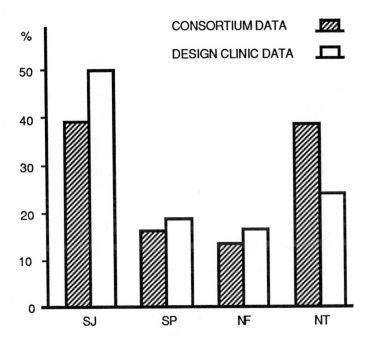

Distribution of ME Design Clinic seniors among the four MBTI defined temperaments.

Figure 5.2

CREATIVITY

One of the most valued traits in an engineer is his ability to develop a wide range of ideas and alternatives for a problem situation. This creative skill for demand ideation is an ability that all students can develop. However, the diagnostics show that the majority of engineering students are sensing (S types) who inherently shun the ambiguities and idealistic uncertainties of a creative approach. The creative process in engineering is basically an intuitive (N) type characteristic.

In the Clinic, I use two diagnostics to help the student identify his preference and skill level as it relates to his proficiency for demand ideation (brainstorming, et al.). The Remote Associates Test (RAT) has been identified as an instrument that shows high correlation with creative performance. Figure 5.3 shows the profile of percentile scores of the Clinic students. The diagnostic seems to correlate too closely with GPA (intelligence) since it is a word association test. Foreign students unfamiliar with our language idioms fail miserably and account for most of the score in the IV quartile. This diagnostic does not measure their ability. In search for a more meaningful measure of creative potential, I have been using the Dogmatism Indicator.* This instrument dentifies a preference for open-mindedness (willingness to accept alternatives and new concepts) vs. closed-mindedness (conservative, inflexible adherence to adopted ideas and concepts). The summary data in Figure 5.4 shows the majority of the students indicate openmindedness. However, the correlation to MBTI type characteristics confirms that SJs tend to be more closed-minded and can be expected to preform poorly in ideation activities.

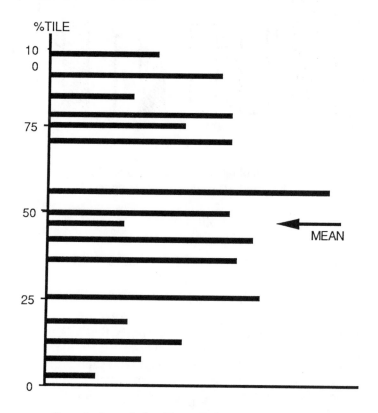

Remote Association Test (RAT) frequency distribution
of percentile scores, MEDC seniors, N = 155

Figure 5.3

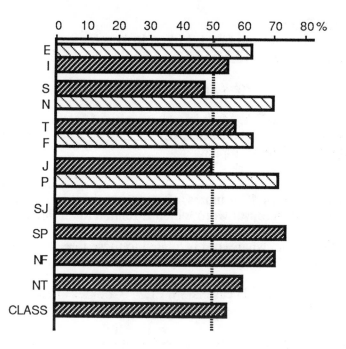

Dogmatism (attitude flexibility) - Open-mindedness
scores vs. MBTI type, MEDC seniors, N = 167

Figure 5.4

In coaching students, I contend that everyone can be proficient in demand ideation. I counsel the SJs that they aren't good at it primarily because they prefer to avoid doing it -- they can do it as well as anyone else when they have to. I illustrate the point by noting that the Is avoid making phone calls or verbal presentations. They prefer to let the Es do it since Es love to talk anyway.

The diagnostic instruments used in the ME Design Clinic program were obtained from the following sources:

Myer-Briggs Personality Indicator
    Center for Application of Psychological Type, Inc.
    414 Southwest 7th Terrace
    Gainsville, FL 32601
    904/375-0160

Remote Association Test
    Houghton Mifflin Co.
    Wayside Road
    Burlington, MD 01803

<u>Dogmatism Scale</u>
Form E - Taken from Ch. 4, Milton Rokeach,
<u>The Open and Closed Mind</u>, Basic Books, NY, 1960

Remote Associates Test

Created by: Siarnoff A. Mednick, University of Michigan
The test can be purchased from:
Houghton Mifflin Company
New York, New York

- The test takes 40 minutes. It presents three words and asks you to find a fourth word which is related to all three.

  For example, what word is related to these three?
  cookies . . . sixteen . . . heart

  The answer in this case is SWEET! Cookies are sweet, sweet is parts of the phrase "sweet sixteen" and the word sweetheart.

- The test will be scored in class and you will obtain a percentile score showing your standing relative to others.

- A class profile will be prepared showing the distribution of percentile scores.

About the Myers-Briggs Type Indicator

- A 130 item, 30 minute, force choice instrument that identifies the basic preference profile of your own personality.

- The test determines whether you are:
  An Introvert (I) or an Extrovert (E)
  A Sensing (S) type or an Intuitive (N) type
  A Thinking (T) type or a Feeling (F) type
  A Perceptive (P) type or a Judging (J) type

- Your Psychological Type Indicator defines you as one of the 16 combinations of any four of the 8 possible characteristics:

ISTJ	ISFJ
ISTP	ISFP
ESTP	ESFP
ESTJ	ESFJ
INFJ	INTJ
INFP	INTP
ENFP	ENTP
ENFJ	ENTJ

- Type tests of engineers shown that various engineering disciplines attract a different clustering of personalities.

- Test booklets and answer sheets can be obtained from:
  Consulting Psychologists Press, Inc.
  577 College Avenue
  Palo Alto, CA 94306 - Phone 415/326-4448

- Machine scoring and books describing type characteristics can be obtained from:
  Center for Application of Psychological Type
  414 S.W. 7th Terrace
  Gainsville, FL 32601 - Phone 904/375-0160

- Test data show that different careers attract different personality types. In engineering, two thirds of the engineers have Introverts (I), Sensing (S), Thinking (T), and Judging (J), personality characteristics, that is, the stereotype engineer has an ISTJ personality.

MYERS BRIGGS TYPE INDICATOR DATA
ENGINEERING FRESHMEN N = 3030

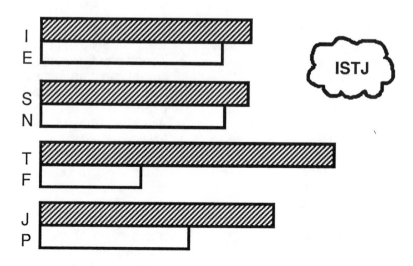

Figure 5.5

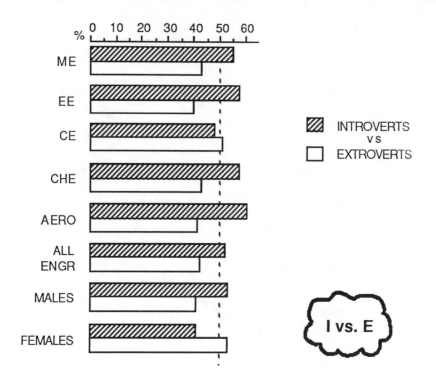

Figure I vs E

Introverts

- Like quiet for concentration.
- Tend to be careful with de
  tails, dislike sweeping
  statements.
- Have trouble remembering
  names and faces.
- Tend not to mind working on
  one project for a long time
  uninterruptedly.
- Are interested in the idea
  behind their job.
- Dislike telephone intrusions
  and interruptions.
- Like to think a lot before they
  act, sometimes without acting.
- Work contentedly alone.
- Have some problems
  communicating.

Extroverts

- Like variety and action.
- Tend to be faster, dislike
  complicated procedures.
- Are often good at greeting
  people.
- Are often impatient with
  long, slow jobs.
- Are interested in the results
  of their job, in getting it
  done and in how other
  people do it.
- Often don't mind the
  interruption of answering
  the telephone.
- Often act quickly,
  sometimes without
  thinking.
- Like to have people around.
- Usually communicate well.

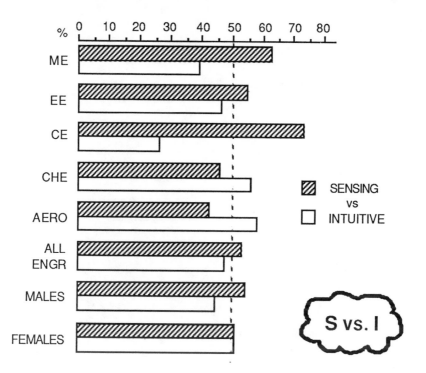

Figure S vs I

Sensing Types

- Dislike new problems unless there are standard ways to solve them.
- Like an established routine.
- Enjoy using skills already learned more than learning new ones.
- Work more steadily, with realistic idea of how long it will usually take.
- Must usually work all the way through to reach a conclusion.
- Are impatient when the details get complicated.
- Rarely trust inspirations, and don't usually get inspired.
- Seldom make errors of fact.
- Tend to be good at precise work.

Intuitive Types

- Like solving new problems.
- Dislike doing the same thing over and over again.
- Enjoy learning a new skill more than using it.
- Work in bursts of energy powered by enthusiasm, with slack periods in between.
- Put two and two together quickly.
- Are patient with complicated situations.
- Are impatient with routine details.
- Follow their inspirations, good or bad.
- Often get their facts a bit wrong.
- Dislike taking time for precision.

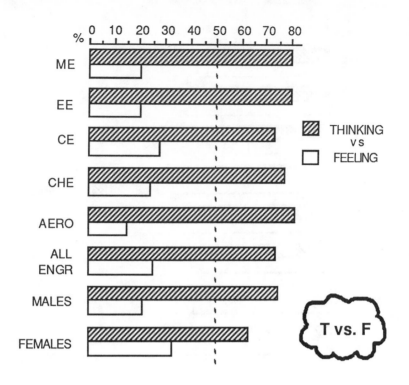

Figure T vs F

Thinking Types
- Are relatively unemotional and uninterested in people's feelings.
- May hurt people's feelings without knowing it.
- Like analysis and putting things into logical order. Can get along without harmony.
- Tend to decide impersonally, sometimes ignoring people's wishes.
- Need to be treated fairly.
- Are able to reprimand people or fire them when necessary.
- Tend to relate well only to other thinking types.
- May seem hard-hearted.

Feeling Types
- Tend to be very aware of other people and their feelings.
- Enjoy pleasing people, even in unimportant things.
- Like harmony. Efficiency may be badly disturbed by office feuds.
- Often let decisions be influenced by their own or other people's personal likes and wishes.
- Need occasional praise.
- Dislike telling people un pleasant things.
- Relate well to most people.
- Tend to be sympathetic.

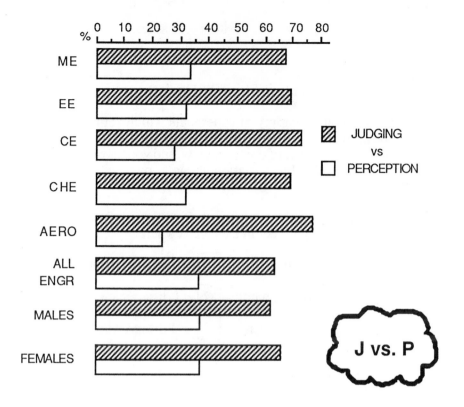

Figure J vs P

Judging Types	*Perceptive Types*
• Best when they can plan their own work and follow the plan.	• Tend to be good at adapting to changing situations.
• Like to get things settled and wrapped up.	• Don't mind leaving things open for alterations.
• May decide too quickly.	• May have trouble making decisions.
• May dislike to interrupt the project they are on for a more urgent one.	• Many start too many projects and have difficulty in finishing them.
• May not notice new things that need to be done.	• May postpone unpleasant jobs.
• Want only the essentials needed to get on with it.	• Want to know all about a new job.
• Tend to be satisfied once they reach a judgment on a thing, situation or person.	• Tend to be curious and welcome new light on a thing, situation or person.

Name _____

MBTI Type: _____

Attitude Flexibility Indicator

The following are a variety of statements which stimulate a wide range of agreement and disagreement among the general public. They represent a variety of points of view, and you may find yourself expressing considerable variation in your own agreement with them.

In the box next to each statement, write +1, +2, +3, or -1, -2, -3, depending on how you feel in each case where:

+1 = I agree a little.   -1 = I disagree a little.

+2 = I agree on the whole.   -2 = I disagree on the whole.

+3 = I agree very much.   -3 = I disagree very much.

1. The United States and Russia have just about nothing in common.

2. The highest form of government is a democracy and the highest form of democracy is a government run by those who are more intelligent.

3. Even though freedom of speech for all groups is a worthwhile goal, it is unfortunately necessary to restrict the freedom of certain political groups.

4. It is only natural that a person would have much better acquaintance with ideas he believes in than with ideas he opposes.

5. Man on his own is a helpless and miserable creature.

6. Fundamentally, the world we live in is a pretty lonesome place.

7. Most people just don't give a "damn" for others.

8. I'd like it if I could find someone who would tell me how to solve my personal problems.

☐ 9. It is only natural for a person to be rather fearful of the future.

☐ 10. There is so much to be done and so little time to do it in.

☐ 11. Once I get wound up in a heated discussion, I just can't stop.

☐ 12. In a discussion, I often find it necessary to repeat myself several times to make sure I am being understood.

☐ 13. In a heated discussion, I generally become so absorbed in what I am going to say that I forget to listen to what the others are saying.

☐ 14. It is better to be a dead hero than a live coward.

☐ 15. While I don't like to admit this even to myself, my secret ambition is to become a great man, like Einstein, or Beethoven, or Shakespeare.

☐ 16. The main thing in life is for a person to want to do something important.

☐ 17. If given the chance, I would do something of great benefit to the world.

☐ 18. In the history of mankind, there has probably been just a handful of really great thinkers.

☐ 19. There are a number of people I have come to hate because of the things they stand for.

☐ 20. A man who does not believe in some great cause has not really lived.

☐ 21. It is only when a person devotes himself to an ideal or cause that life becomes meaningful.

☐ 22. Of all the different philosophies which exist in this world, there is probably only one which is correct.

☐ 23. A person who gets enthusiastic about too many causes is likely to be a pretty "wishy-washy" sort of person.

☐ 24. To compromise with our political opponents is dangerous because it usually leads to the betrayal of our own side.

☐ 25. When it comes to differences of opinion in religion, we must be careful not to compromise with those who believe differently from the way we do.

☐ 26. In times like these, a person must be pretty selfish if he considers principally his own happiness.

☐ 27. The worst crime a person could commit is to attack publicly the people who believe in the same thing he does.

☐ 28. In times like these, it is often necessary to be more on guard against ideas put out by people or groups in one's own camp than by those in the opposing camp.

☐ 29. A group which tolerates too much differences of opinions among its own members cannot exist for long.

☐ 30. There are two kinds of people in this world: those who are for the truth and those who are against the truth.

☐ 31. My blood boils whenever a person stubbornly refuses to admit he's wrong.

☐ 32. A person who thinks primarily of his own happiness is beneath contempt.

☐ 33. Most of the ideas which get printed nowadays aren't worth he paper they are printed on.

☐ 34. In this complicated world of ours, the only way we can know what's going on is to rely on leaders and experts who can be trusted.

☐ 35. It is often desirable to reserve judgment about what's going on until one has had a chance to hear the opinions of those one respects.

☐ 36. In the long run, the best way to live is to pick friends and associates whose tastes and beliefs are the same as one's own.

☐ 37. The present is all too often full of unhappiness. It is only the future that counts.

☐ 38. If a man is to accomplish his mission in life, it is sometimes necessary to gamble "all or nothing at all."

☐ 39. Unfortunately, a good many people with whom I have discussed important social and moral problems don't really understand what's going on.

☐ 40. Most people just don't know what's good for them.

Scoring

1. Add all the + numbers:Total: + ◯

2. Add all the - numbers:Total: - ◯

Add the + total and - total (algebraically):

Total Score: { + ◯
              { - ◯

(Circle Sign)

RELATIVE DISTRIBUTION OF PERSONALITY TEMPERAMENT

ENGINEERING STUDENTS N: 3030

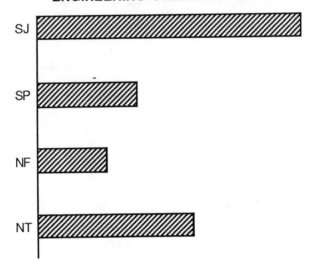

Figure 5.10

IDEATION TECHNIQUE

Creativity:

A Misunderstood Phenomenon:

- Everyone has creative potential
- Creativity and intelligence don't relate
- Your creative potential can be improved by training

Who Is Creative?

The Creative Guy is:

- Intelligent (IQ: 100-140) - curious
- Aggressive - outspoken - objective
- Independent - seeks autonomy - privacy
- Dedicated to his tasks - tenacious
- Hard worker - unimpressed by status
- Doesn't value job security
- Can easily accept failure - gullible
- A clown - good sense of humor - accepts chaos
- Nonconformist - enjoys change - new ideas
- Wants supervision and sympathetic listener

Levels of Creativity:

- Expressive - spontaneous, impulsive
- Productive - practical alternatives
- Inventive - developing new ways
- Innovative - concept break-through
- Emergentive - extension of awareness

Creativity Hang-Ups:

- Fear technical area is over your head
- Tendency to think small - instead of "way out"
- Wanting to be practical
- Tendency to deal with effect rather than cause
- Can't focus on what needs to be done - want to look at what the boss wants
- Looking for gimmicks - avoiding the "obvious"

Negativity - Attributes of the Uncreative:

- Resistance to change
- Desire for conformity
- Competitive jealousy - cynicism
- Desire for security - order - routine
- Fear of ridicule and failure
- Distrust of wild ideas
- No desire to experiment

Demand Ideation:

- The "Trigger-word" Technique
- The Checklist Technique
- The Morphological Chart
- The Attribute-Seeking Technique
- The Gordon Technique
- The Brainstorming Technique

The Attribute-Seeking Technique

Devise a New Lawn Mower
  Attributes:
- Grass-blade cutting
- Propulsion over lawn surface
- Operator control
- Power supply
- Trimmings disposal

- Put to other uses?
- Adapt? like-copy-suggest
- Modify? change-color-order-shape
- Magnify? bigger-longer-extra-add
- Minify? subtract-lower-shrink-cut off
- Substitute? replace-other-what else
- Rearrange? scramble-alter sequence
- Reverse? opposite-backward-invert
- Combine? blend-add to-hook up with

"Trigger-word" Samples

- MOVE
melt-peel-cut-tear
slice-screw-whirl-roll
explode-bend-unravel

- GET OPEN
float-push-roll-slide
shove-lift-drag-slip
leap-run-fly-pull

- PUT IN
squirt-drop-pour-fall
tilt-fold-ram-knock
construct-dump-swing

- GET SHUT
bend-wrap-weld-clip
bolt-roll-solder-lock
nail-pin-press-mold

Idea Stimulators:

Look for similarities
Look for associated equipment and conditions in the vicinity

Look for contrast:
- Exaggerate
- Magnify
- Minify
- Modify
- Reverse
- Switch
- Rearrange
- Opposites

Look for inversions:
- Backwards
- Upside down
- Change places
- Stop the moving-move the stationary
- Inside out
- Mirror image
- Left for right

IDEATION FOLLOW-UP

What to do with all those ideas!

Evaluate creativity -
- Every idea has shortcomings -- look for what's good about it!
- Can it be modified? Combined with others?

- What else can you do with it?

Every idea is valuable - even the crazy ones!

MORPHOLOGICAL APPROACH TO IDEATION

One of the most useful techniques for idea getting is the morphological chart -- it categorizes the requirements and characteristics needed and helps focus the search for alternatives. It is a systematic and categorical approach to the creative design process. It involves the construction of a table in which:

a) The parameters (independent characteristics) of the problem situations are listed in a column.

b) The ideas for achieving each parameter are tabulated in rows.

In considering the problem of devising a mechanical device to connect a 10-year-old boy (energy source) to the boat to provide a system for propelling the boat, you devise a list of "basic attributes needed." The basic attributes (sample listed in left column, see chart page 5-24) define the various characteristics of the system that must be achieved. (If you think of others, list them).

For example, "input motion" states a requirement to define what kind of input motion the boy must produce to activate the mechanism. (How the energy is to be delivered). The "input source" defines the part of the boy's body or body movement ability that will be used to produce the input motion of the device, and so on.

Fill in the table. If you happen to be inspired and run out of space, make a bigger table.

After you have filled in the table, survey the rows and columns and list several combinations of ideas by taking one idea from each row. Compile three or four interesting combinations and put them in order of apparent practibility.

The morphological approach is a powerful method for selecting the appropriate mechanism classes to be used in synthesizing the needed motion requirement. The chart is filled out with alternatives listed without thought to practicalities. After a host of alternatives are in sight, then you should make value judgments as to which combination best fits the various constraints and requirements. It will soon boil down to a few combinations worthy of further exploration and development one way or another of this process of selection will have to be done before you begin the synthesis process.

Morphological Chart Application

Design of a Child-Powered Outdoor Merry-Go-Round

Step 1. List all the things about a child-powered merry-go-round that are going to require a decision or, putting it another way -- list all the questions you would ask: For Example:

1. How will the turning platform be connected to the ground so it will revolve?
2. What part of the child's body will be used to provide the turning force?
3. What will the kids have to do to make it turn? Can any number of kids be used to power the thing?
4. What transmits the kids' input to turning effort on the turning platform?
5. What shapes can the platform have to enhance the whole system?

These questions define the "attributes" of the design for which a number of alternatives must be considered before a decision can be made. They are items that go in the left hand column of the Morphological Chart:

1. Turning device
2. Child input
3. Input method
4. Power transmission
5. Platform shape

For each of the five listed attributes, use the chart to list in a horizontal row all the different possible alternatives. This is the creative ideation "brainstorming" phase of the process. You list everything you can WITHOUT worrying whether they are practical or even possible. The objective is to get as many alternatives for each of the five attributes as you can:

For example, in filling out the chart:

For attribute #2, the child input - both legs, one leg, both arms, one arm, arms and legs, body weight, etc.

For attribute #3, the input method - running on ground, turning crank, running on treadmill, push lever, pull lever, foot pedals, pulling rope, turnstyle, etc.

When you have filled in the chart as much as you can for each attribute (question), you have many alternative combinations to choose from. That is, select an alternative from each row to make a combined system.

The next obvious step is to decide which of the combinations has the best overall appeal, practicality, safety, simplicity, etc. This is the process of creative evaluation; list the most attractive combinations from the table and in consultation with others. Give them a + or - rating on each of the criteria you are using (such as safety, ecomony, simplicity, low maintenance, reliability, etc.). The system with the most plus votes should be the most viable choice.

SAMPLE MORPHOLOGICAL IDEATION CHART

For Designing a Manual Propulsion System for a Boat

Basic Attributes Needed	IDEAS (Various Alternatives to be Considered)					
Input Motion						
Input Source						
Input Device						
Output						
Mechanism						
Operator Position						

Chapter 6

THE PLANNING PHASE

INTRODUCTION

The Planning Phase, sometimes referred to as the "analytical" or "evaluation" phase, is that period when judgment is applied to the creative process. This is the screening, sifting, combining process that brings product requirements, marketing features and function characteristics into the transition from idea to solution. However, applying judgment does not mean that the roadblocks squelched during speculation now become valid. The positive attitude developed during speculation must be maintained throughout this and subsequent phases in the job plan.

The planning phase deals with judging and selecting ideas against quantitative and qualitative criteria that are valid to the problem or issue being analyzed. Judgment will be applied to narrow and pare out ideas leading to the development of implementable solutions. In this phase, there will be a transition from divergent thinking to convergent thinking. We want to remain open-minded while we go through the judgment of ideas and finally come to a gradual stop with a recommended solution. The roadblocks, discussed earlier, can still act as "killer phrases" and should be avoided. Roadblocks will tend to take on a different form during planning. Judgment starting with "no, because..." should be avoided; this opening should be viewed as a roadblock. Answers starting with that phrase are not only negative, but if left unchallenged, will "slam the door" against further analysis or consideration.

Many ideas can be made to work if certain problems are overcome. A problem should not be the cause for rejection until it is objectively evaluated. Therefore, judgment responses should begin with "Yes, if ..." This translates the problem to an issue and invites further speculation on how to overcome any restrictions.

A "Yes, if ..." response will often surface a very practical solution that would otherwise be rejected as being impractical. Ideas should be accepted or rejected based on the feasibility of implementation, given the objectives and parameters of the solution sought, rather than emotions. One idea may be very practical if a minor sub-problem can be resolved. For another idea, it may be that a large research project will be required to advance the state of the art before the idea can be implemented. The latter may be rejected because of the time and cost involved. Unless the conditions have been identified for implementation, rejection is based on roadblocks, prejudices, or ignorance. For some ideas, the "Yes, if ..." answer is obviously impractical for meeting the requirements of the solution. For others, the feasibility is not as obvious and requires more in-depth answers. The "Yes, if ..." answer may indicate that a modification of the idea will eliminate or minimize an implementation problem. The "Yes, if ..." approach encourages the use of ideas where the "No, because ..." approach discourages ideas.

QUANTITATIVE AND QUALITATIVE SCREENING

A solution to any problem must satisfy some requirement(s). The requirement(s) may be specified in quantitative terms (must operate between 0 degrees F and 120 degrees F; shall operate on 110 volt household wiring) or in qualitative terms (shall be simple to operate; shall be easily maintained). Quantitative requirements must be met within the measurable limits. Qualitative requirements are subject to a degree of attainment.

In the information phase, a number of functions were identified and the requirement for the functions specified. In the speculation phase, ideas were generated for each of these functions that might be useful as a solution. In this phase, the ideas are evaluated against the requirements for each function.

The requirements imposed on the solution were at least partially disclosed in the fact-finding part of the information phase. Questions were raised and answers obtained. That information, and additional information if required, will be used for the evaluation of the ideas. The fact-finding was performed early so the problem statement could be properly specified. The information will be used in this phase to screen ideas.

During the evaluation procedure, we will address the following issues:

    1.   Against what criteria is selection to be made?
            Quantitative -- measurable values
            Qualitative -- non-measurable criteria
    2.   Qualitative idea screen
            Looking for a sponsor
    3.   Quantitative idea screen
            "Yes, if ..."
    4.   Qualitative screening for surviving ideas
            What is the relative importance of the criteria?
            How well does each idea meet the criteria?

Pre-Screening

The speculation phase, if successful, resulted in a great number and variety of ideas. These ideas were spontanteously generated with no thought to their practicality. Only their relationship to the function being explored was considered. Being blessed with a large number of random ideas, the task team must now pare them down to a manageable quantity before evaluating the ideas against the solutions criteria. This involves a member of the task team asking if any members object to setting an idea aside. If any member objects without further qualification or discussion, the idea remains for the next evaluation procedure.

The First Screening

In evaluating ideas against requirements, the first screening should be made against quantitative requirements. If the "Yes, if ..." answer does not reveal a practical method of meeting the quantitative requirement, the idea may not be a good candidate for a solution.

If an idea appears to have considerable merit but cannot meet some quantitative requirement, the idea should be marked for study with that particular requirement investigated to determine whether the requirement, or its limits, are valid. Requirements should be challenged when they cause rejection of what otherwise may be a solution worthy of further consideration. All ideas that survive the quantitative screening are considered to be technically feasible although there may be considerable variance in the practicality and acceptability of the ideas.

Qualitative Screening Techniques

The qualitative screening process is subject to emotions, roadblocks, and prejudices and requires the use of techniques to minimize the bias. This phase will mainly be concerned with qualitative screening techniques. Some techniques work better than others with certain problems or with a certain mix of people. The purpose of evaluation is to be as objective as possible in the final solution. Whatever technique best achieves this goal is the one to use. The techniques presented here include: Numerical Evaluation by Paired Comparison, Rank and Rate, and Delphi -- Gut Feeling Index (GFI) (see forms at end of chapter).

In this approach, each idea is evaluated as to its relative merit with each other idea -- one at a time. This breaks down the evaluation into several mini-decisions, which tend to remove or minimize the bias. Not only are ideas evaluated against each other, but they are also evaluated as to whether the idea is significantly, moderately, or minimally better than another idea.

The following illustrates the mechanics of this technique. Assuming that we have five ideas we want to objectively evaluate for the best one, we would list them and identify each with a key letter. Using the pencil as an example (illustrated in Chapter 1), a short list may appear as follows:

Table 6.1

KEY LETTER	DESCRIPTION OF IDEA	VALUE
A	Eliminate paint	
B	Reduce length of lead	
C	Remove eraser	
D	Stain wood in lieu of paint	
E	Make body out of plastic	

The next step would be to evaluate idea "A" with respect to idea "B." Is "A" or "B" a better solution for the problem, considering the cost/function contribution and sell features? Is it significantly better (value of 3), moderately better (value of 2) or minimally better (value of 1)? The scorecard for the evaluation can be made on the following matrix, where each relationship has an intersection block. Assuming that idea "B" was judged moderately better than idea "A," the "B-2" would be posted in the "A-B" intersection block.

Table 6.2

	B	C	D	E
A	B - 2	A - 1	D - 2	A - 1
B		B - 3	B - 2	B - 2
C			D - 1	C - 1
D				D - 2

Significant 3
Moderate 2
Minimal 1

By adding the values for each idea, the values can be posted:
A = 1 + 1 = 2, B = 2 + 3 + 2 + 2 = 9, etc.

Table 6.3

KEY LETTER	DESCRIPTION OF IDEA	VALUE
A	Eliminate paint	2
B	Reduce length of lead	9
C	Remove eraser	1
D	Stain wood in lieu of paint	5
E	Make body out of plastic	0

From this evaluation, we would select "B" as the best idea compared to all the other ideas, with "D" as our next choice. This technique can be used to determine the relative evaluation of various types of factors such as the relative importance of different requirements, the determination of priorities, the relative evaluation of performance, and the relative selection of products such as which car or which house to buy.

Rank and Rate is an extension of the Numerical Evaluation by Paired Comparisons technique. This technique matches the ideas against the requirements and then selects those that best meet the requirements. The Rank and Rate technique has two variables: the importance of the requirements and the ability of the idea to satisfy the requirements.

Each requirement is ranked according to its relative importance to the other requirements. This is a subjective decision, but the bias can be minimized by using the Numerical Evaluation by Paired Comparison, a consensus of opinion by the problem-solving team members, or through consultation with those most responsible for implementing the decision. In evaluating a product, the customer, represented by marketing and sales, should be included.

There are many ranking techniques. One technique is to list the requirements from the most important to the least important and assign a sequential rating number (1, 2, 3, 4, ...) with the most important having the highest number. This technique does not give a true quantitative measure of the difference between one requirement and another. A requirement rated "4" may not be twice as important as a requirement rated "2." Another ranking technique is to assign points to the total requirements -- such as 100. Each requirement is assigned a value such that the total value of the requirements equals 100. This technique provides a better indication of a quantitative difference of importance and also permits assignment of equal value to requirements that are considered of equal importance, but it is best to discourage ranking requirements as "equal." If the Numerical Evaluation by Paired Comparison is used to rank the requirements, the resulting value from that evaluation can be used directly or converted to a percent of 100, with each requirement having a different pie segment, separated by at least 3 points.

The rating of each idea as to how well it can fulfill each of the requirements can be rated as excellent, good, fair, poor, or none, and assigned respective numerical designations such as 4, 3, 2, 1, or 0. The summation of the rating times the rank will give a score for each idea. The higher scores will be the ideas that have the greatest potential of meeting the requirements for the solution.

In the simulated pencil example, the basic function "make marks" is not disturbed by the ideas offered. Therefore, it can be set aside while the other requirements are considered and ranked. An example:

Prioritizing Requirements (Pencil Example)

Description

No. 1	the ability to "expose" lead (sharpen pencil)		30 pts.
No. 2	the structural integrity (distribute load)		15 pts.
No. 3	the functional feature "remove marks"		10 pts.
No. 4	aesthetic appearance (perceived value)		45 pts.
	Total		100 pts.

A matrix analysis would appear as follows in Table 6.4.

Table 6.4

Idea	Requirement				Total Score
	No 1-30 pts	No 2-15 pts	No 3-10 pts	No 4-45 pts	
A	3 / 90	3 / 45	4 / 40	1 / 45	220
B	3 / 90	4 / 60	4 / 40	4 / 180	370
C	4 / 120	4 / 60	0 / 0	2 / 90	270
D	3 / 90	3 / 45	4 / 40	3 / 135	300
E	1 / 30	4 / 60	2 / 20	3 / 135	245

Excellent - 4, Good - 3, Fair - 2, Poor - 1, None - 0

In this example, idea "B" (reduce length of lead) is the most promising candidate -- (3 x 30) + (4 x 10) + (4 x 45) = 370. The second best idea is "D." Additional efforts to improve or combine the higher score ideas should be encouraged. Since the requirements are qualitative, a perfect score of 400 is not required.

DELPHI - GUT FEEL INDEX (GFI)

The Delphi technique was first developed by Olaf Helmer at the Rand Corporation and has since been modified for evaluating ideas. The Delphi, as originally developed, is a technique that attempts to achieve a consensus of opinion that an event will or will not take place within a given period of time. These events are generally future events such as predicting a technological breakthrough. The technique is conducted by questionnaires mailed to experts in the subject under investigation. The participants' identities are not known to each other to avoid intimidation by a dominant personality. The responses to the questionnaire are collected and analyzed to determine those events for which there is a high correlation of opinion and those events for which there is low correlation. Those events where there is low correlation are resubmitted to the participants indicating why those at the extreme ends of the evaluation felt the way they did. The recycling of these questionnaires, along with views, are for the purpose of attempting to change the views of the participants to get a tighter correlation. Where correlation cannot be achieved within three cycles of questionnaires, these events are considered as having a high degree of uncertainty about the future trend. The events of high correlation will most likely occur within the time frame of the consensus opinion.

The Delphi technique not only discloses areas of high correlation, but it also tends to become a self-fulfilling prophecy. The experts are generally those who are the most likely to influence the occurrence of an event. A high correlation will usually indicate an effort by the experts to work toward the same goal.

The Gut Feel Index (GFI) utilizes the underlying theories of the Delphi technique. The ideas that were generated during the speculation phase were earlier screened to eliminate those ideas that could not meet the quantitative requirements. The second screening process is to go over the surviving ideas with the originator explaining what he or she had in mind. If any team member feels the idea is worthy of further consideration, then the idea is retained. If no one feels the idea is worth further consideration, then that idea is discarded. We are now ready to select those ideas that will be expanded into the proposals for development.

GFI Process
1. Pre-Screening
2. Sponsorship
3. For/Against
4. Average Score

The Gut Feel Index contends that when the individual team member intuitively quantifies an idea for its merit, the average rating of the team, especially if they represent mixed disciplines, will reflect the probability of successful implementation well within acceptable accuracy limits. This assumes that the disciplines bear directly on the problem, and the individual is drawing upon his or her knowledge and experience in making the assessment.

In evaluating the surviving candidates, each member assigns a number from one to ten to each idea reflecting the degree of his or her confidence that the idea can achieve both its <u>technical</u> and <u>economic</u> expectations. Before an average is computed, the team member with the highest evaluation explains why he is so confident it will work, and the low evaluator explains his lack of confidence. After allowing for any changes, the average is computed and a Gut Feel Index is assigned to the idea.

The process involves giving each member of the team a suite of playing cards, from 1 to 10. After the presentations are made, the team members expose their cards simultaneously. This reduces the chance that one team member's opinion will dominate the others. To avoid "sitting on the fence," the "five" is withdrawn from the suite of cards, requiring that a favorable or unfavorable choice be made.

The individual vote is based on 3 qualifying parameters:
1. Can the idea be made to work?
2. Can it be implemented in a reasonable time, for a reasonable investment?
3. Will it contribute to the goals?

In the event that a large number of ideas survive the initial and secondary screening making the scoring process rather long and involved, a supplementary screening can be performed prior to GFI scoring. Each team member selects a specified number of best and worst ideas from the list of surviving candidate ideas. The selections can be posted on a scorecard, shown in Figure 6.1. In the example shown in Figure 6.1, team member "A" selected ideas 1, 3, and 6 as the three best and 5, 7, and 26 as the three worst. Only those ideas that have positive selections, but no negatives, are retained as candidates (ideas 2, 4, 6, and 8 in Figure 6.1). Those ideas that have a mixture of positives and negatives are discussed to see if the views of one can influence the views of the other. After reporting any changes, the positive only ideas are evaluated for GFI scoring as previously described. The GFI score is the average of the 1 - 10 rating assigned by each team member to each idea.

The GFI score indicates the degree of risk, as perceived by the task team, associated with the successful implementation of the idea. The following Risk Parameter Guide describes the degree of risk usually associated with a GFI score.

CATEGORY NO.   DESCRIPTION OF RISK   GFI RANGE

I	Recommendation has low technical risk, immediate pay-back, low investment, no additional testing or major evaluations required. Changes are not customer sensitive.	7.5-10
II	Recommendation has some technical unknowns and unconfirmed pay-backs and investments. Minor test and evaluation/ investigation required. Good pay-back potential. Low customer visibility.	6-7.4
III	Recommendation has good pay-back potential, needs engineering development program. No new technology. May need market reaction; could be implemented on this product later. New approach, but performs same function.	4.5-5.9
IV	Recommendation has different concept to perform higher order function. High (unknown) technical risks, unknown but potentially very high pay-back possible. Represents second generation approach. Some new technology, introduced. Low probability of affecting current product. Needs full market survey.	2-4.4

Note: A GFI of less than 2.0 would not be recommended

The Risk Parameter Guide can be used to outline a program where the Category I ideas can be implemented immediately and the ideas in the other categories can be programmed for further investigation, development or research.

A GFI score that does not correspond to the category description of the risk that might be anticipated should be discussed by the group. A high GFI score on a high risk idea would indicate strong group confidence in the idea. A low GFI score on a low risk idea would show weak support for the idea.

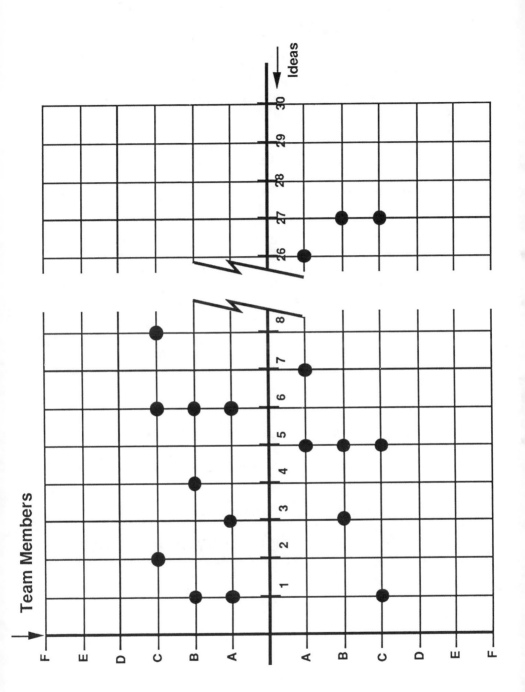

Figure 6.1

COMPILATION OF IDEAS

The evaluation process is intended to provide visibility of those ideas that best meet the constraints imposed on the solution of the problem. If the problem involves looking for solutions at higher level functions and lower level functions, it is probable that some of the lower level solutions would not be applicable if certain higher level solutions were selected. It is now necessary to look at the various surviving solutions in the context of a total system. If all the highest rated solutions for each function could be brought together into a complete working system, we would have an ideal solution. However, compromises may have to be made.

Various scenarios can be developed by constructing problem identification diagrams (hierarchical, FAST) with different solutions inserted. The systems that best describe workable solutions are selected for developing the details of the systems, including the cost to implement the ideas. The execution phase will crystallize the concepts to determine the lowest cost of the workable solutions for final selection.

The several forms at the end of this chapter are included to assist in posting and evaluating data.

CHAPTER 6 QUESTIONS

1. The Planning Phase is also know by other names, such as
    _____ and _____.

2. What is the purpose of the Planning Phase?

3. True or False: Once into the Planning Phase, roadblocks are permitted to evaluate the risk or down side of an idea (explain).

PLANNING PHASE
GUT FEEL INDEX

DATE _____

FUNCTION _____ PAGE NO. ___									FUNCTION _____ PAGE NO. ___								
Idea Spec. No	Speculation Total, Each Team Member						Team Total	Cate-gory No.	Idea Spec. No	Speculation Total, Each Team Member						Team Total	Cate-gory No.
	A	B	C	D	E	F				A	B	C	D	E	F		

PERFORMANCE CRITERIA

QUANTITATIVE REQUIREMENTS	QUANTITATIVE MEASURE

QUANTITATIVE REQUIREMENTS	WEIGHT OF EACH
TOTAL	

SUMMARY EVALUATION

KEY LETTER	DESCRIPTION	VALUE
A		
B		
C		
D		
E		
F		
G		
H		
I		
J		
K		
L		
M		
N		

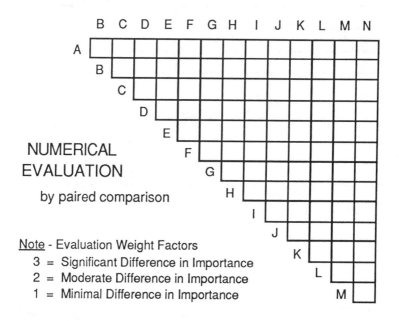

NUMERICAL EVALUATION
by paired comparison

Note - Evaluation Weight Factors
3 = Significant Difference in Importance
2 = Moderate Difference in Importance
1 = Minimal Difference in Importance

RANK AND RATE

CANDIDATE IDEAS SURVIVING QUANTITATIVE SCREENING	QUALITATIVE REQUIREMENTS					
	NO. 1 WT. __	NO. 2 WT. __	NO. 3 WT. __	NO. 4 WT. __	NO. 5 WT. __	TOTAL SCORE
1.						
2.						
3.						
4.						
5.						
6.						
7.						
8.						
9.						
10.						
11.						
12.						
13.						
14.						
15.						
16.						
17.						
18.						
19.						
20.						

Use additional sheets as required.

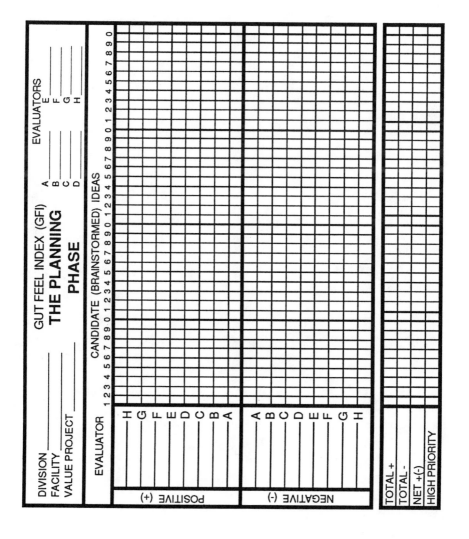

GUT FEEL INDEX (GFI)
THE PLANNING
PHASE

DIVISION
FACILITY
VALUE PROJECT

EVALUATORS
A   E
B   F
C   G
D   H

CANDIDATE (BRAINSTORMED) IDEAS
1 2 3 4 5 6 7 8 9 0 1 2 3 4 5 6 7 8 9 0 1 2 3 4 5 6 7 8 9 0 1 2 3 4 5 6 7 8 9 0

EVALUATOR

POSITIVE (+)
H
G
F
E
D
C
B
A

NEGATIVE (-)
A
B
C
D
E
F
G
H

TOTAL +
TOTAL -
NET +(-)
HIGH PRIORITY

Chapter 7

COST ANALYSIS FOR VALUE ENGINEERING

INTRODUCTION

The basic concepts of Value Engineering discussed and studied thus far were directed toward development of alternate creative approaches for performing defined functions. Through the use of creative techniques, brainstorming, function analysis, and their support disciplines, we have devised a system of comparative analysis by weighing the various features, advantages, and disadvantages. We have seen that tradeoffs do exist. Such tradeoffs represent valid technical approaches if the basic function representing the project under study is the objective of the analysis. Very often intuitive cost reductions accompany the alternates created. This is an area where we may feel one approach is more economical than another, but economic comparisons must be analyzed to justify the recommendations.

In any comparison there are certain operations, procedures, material, assemblies, support functions, etc., that are common to all of the proposals. Since we are concerned with which approach is most cost effective it is not necessary to evaluate the cost of comparable items. Only those noncomparable costs require evaluation to determine the economic differences between alternates. However, with this approach percentage cost differentials cannot be used to express savings since total costs are not calculated. This and other characteristics of Value Engineering cost analysis will be discussed in subsequent sections.

When making a comparative analysis, the cost comparison phase represents half of that functional-cost balance we are trying to evaluate. The emphasis placed on this phase should be treated with as much importance as the function compatibility of the equipment being considered. The Value Engineer should no more think of guessing at the cost than an electrical or structural engineer guesses at a technical approach. Cost can and should be analyzed and tested with the same degree of proficiency as any technical consideration. However, cost analysis, unlike technical analysis, is largely governed by markets, products, policy, and procedures and will, therefore, vary in approaches used by different companies.

Because of the time involved to perform the analysis and the limited number of Value Engineers available in any organization, the total cost of each comparative approach is not usually considered.

PRODUCT COSTS

In presenting this segment of the Value Engineering study, the cost elements will be described in general terms. Value Engineers should consult their finance departments for more explicit definitions and terms used by the parent company.

To start with, let's label and discuss some of those elements which make up product cost.

I. Recurring Costs

   Refers to those costs which are directly chargeable to each manufactured product (per item, per copy) and are repetitive in nature.

   A. Labor

      The direct factory man-hours required to manufacture a product.

      1. Run time - Man-hours to fabricate each unit.This includes handling time, or the time to move or position a part in a machine.

      2. Setup - Man-hours required to prepare and take down machines or fixtures for fabricating each unit. This cost is prorated over the shop lot quantity as prescribed by Production Planning. Setup does not include the time to produce a product -- only the time to prepare the machine for a production run.

   B. Material

      Cost for each unit in terms of purchased material, components, or assemblies. This also includes scrappage and overbuy.

   C. Shipping Costs

      Transportation charges for special projects, if the cost per unit warrants that cost be considered in the evaluation.

   D. Packing

      The material and labor charges associated with the containing of each unit. This is a fruitful area of investigation and should not be ignored. There have been many cases where packaging concepts represent the prime subject for a Value Engineering study. The traffic department is a good source for accumulating and analyzing cost data relative to packing and shipping.

   E. Inspection

      Includes receiving inspection of purchased items and the recurring inspection costs and non-destructive tests verifying that the performance and producibility requirements of a design are being maintained.

II. Non-recurring Costs
The one time costs or investment required to implement the production plan.
A. Engineering
Cost to design, develop and qualify a product, including engineering support and services. Note: In some cases engineering support services are computed as a percentage of design engineering hours. If this is not the case, a check list to determine total engineering requirements should be developed to estimate total engineering costs.
B. Tooling
The costs of tools which are required to manufacture a specific product. Capital tooling is not normally considered as a part of Value Engineering analysis, unless an alternate approach requires an investment in capital tooling to manufacture that product. When assembling, all tooling costs - tool design, planning, tooling, tooling maintenance, tool material and labor - should be included.
C. Test (proof)
The cost to verify the functional integrity, operational and environmental limits of a product. This includes engineering, fixtures, cost to conduct test, reports, etc. Proof tests are "tests to destruction." Therefore, the cost of the product being tested should also be included as expenses.

III. Supporting Costs
A. Overhead -- Operation Expenses
As the name implies, overhead relating to operating expenses, and includes, but is not limited to:
1. Wages and Salaries - labor for supervision, lost time, clerical labor, etc., charged to overhead
2. Provisions - paid vacations and paid holidays
3. Incentive Compensation - year end bonus
4. Social Security Taxes - Federal Old Age Benefits, unemployment benefits
5. Pension Costs
6. Group Insurance and Workman's Compensation
7. Fire and Liability Insurance
8. Corporate Taxes - real estate, personal property
9. Depreciation and Amortization
   (a) depreciation -- capital assets -- long life
   (b) amortization -- accelerated -- short life
10. Maintenance
   (a) machinery and equipment
   (b) maintenance for buildings occupied
11. Rentals of Buildings and Equipment

12. Electricity, Fuel Oil, Coal, Heat, Light, Power, etc. - prorated on the percent of occupancy of buildings
13. Operation Supplies and Expenses - offices, manuals, brochures, small tools, and travel expenses charged to overhead, training and education

B. Overhead -- General

General overhead pertains to the expense involved in maintaining support functions, which do not necessarily relate directly to the company's product line, but are necessary entries in conducting a business. These include, but are not limited to: procurement, industrial relations, personnel, advertising, selling expenses; and extends to cover donations, stocks (regular and transfers), and annual reports. The overhead items in A and B are percentage add-on to the recurring and non-recurring direct labor costs.

C. Overhead -- Burden

Burden refers to staff support expenses related to the manufacture of the product and charged to a program as a percentage of use by that program. Some areas included are production engineering, field support, liaison, Receiving Inspection, Quality Assurance, etc. Without citing specific exceptions, the broad area of technical staff support could be considered in this category. Burden is essentially an overhead expense, but it can be controlled by the program manager.

D. General and Administrative (G & A)

This area, calculated as a percent of total cost, includes Marketing, Finance, Administration, Advanced Design, Research, and corporate expenses, to name a few.

Performing the economic analysis portion of the Value Engineering study, it is not necessary to calculate each item in overhead and G & A. We include these expenses as "loaded" labor rates which are analyzed and adjusted annually by the finance department.

We have only skimmed the surface of the product cost at this juncture. Each of the topics mentioned could be rearranged, reclassified, or redefined in the financial structure of the particular company. The intent is to give the Value Engineer an appreciation for the complexities of determining costs and its use in analysis, not to train the VE in accounting procedures.

Some of the topics which are not mentioned, but require attention in the cost analysis are profit, chargeable vendor expenses, experience curves, work in process (WIP), the treatment of rework & rejection, and break-even analysis. These are discussed in subsequent chapters.

PROBLEM EXAMPLE

To learn how to perform the cost analysis portion of a Value Engineering study, use the following hypothetical situation and evaluate the conditions as they arise.

As a Value Engineer you are asked to evaluate two design proposals. After performing the techniques necessary to create alternates, you find there are two approaches that can be adapted. Both designs are functionally responsive. All that remains for the acceptance of the design is your recommendation based on the cost advantages involved. For the sake of simplicity and the greater emphasis on principles, consider all information not given as comparable. Just evaluate the given information.

Table 7.1

ITEM	PROPOSED DESIGN A	PROPOSED DESIGN B
Material	$150.00 / unit	$50.00 / unit
Setup	150 min / lot	90 min / lot
Run Time	40 min / lot	35 min / lot
Assembly	55 min / unit	55 min / unit
Tools (Company)	110 hours	85 hours
Tools (Vendor)	none	$8,000.00
Engineering	80 hours	90 hours

Comparable Data:
Dollar rate (including overhead)   Lot quantity - 15 units/lot (2 lots)

Manufacturing $60.00/hour   Firm contract - 30 units

Tooling $65.00/hour   Anticipated - 150 units
                              Follow on (additional)

Engineering $80.00/hour

Determine:
1. The cost of each proposed design.
2. The most economical approach.

Determining the cost of each design approach is relatively simple because the problem is set up in its simplest form. However, you should be careful in making your recommendation.

Cost Breakdown

When evaluating the economic portion of a Value Engineering study, it is best to separate the recurring from the non-recurring costs. The reason for this approach will become evident as we analyze the problem in more detail.

The recurring costs should be calculated on a per unit basis, and the non-recurring costs considered as total investment. Therefore, the first step would be the classification of all cost elements as either recurring or non-recurring.

Consider Setup a recurring cost, because it is a direct part of factory labor. Setup can be computed in terms of per units in two ways:

1. $\text{Setup/Unit} = \dfrac{\text{Setup time x Dol/Hr}}{\text{No. of Units/Lot}}$

2. $\text{Setup/Unit} = \dfrac{\text{Setup time x No. of Setups x Dol/Hr}}{\text{Contract Quantity}}$

Using the problem cited in the previous lesson for Proposed Design A, we have the following given information:

$$\text{Setup} = 150 \text{ minutes}$$
$$\text{Number of units per setup} = 15 \text{ units}$$
$$\text{Firm contract of 30 units}$$
$$\text{Labor rate} = \$60.00/\text{ hour}$$

Solving for the setup per unit using the two approaches, we have:

1. $\text{S.U./Unit} = \dfrac{150 \text{ Min/S.U. (60 Dol/Hr)}}{15 \text{ Units/Lot (60 Min/Hr)}} = \$10.00/\text{Unit}$

2. $\text{S.U./Unit} = \dfrac{150 \text{Min/S.U. (60 Dol/Hr)}}{30 \text{ Units (60 Dol/Hr)}} = \$10.00/\text{Unit}$

Since the results in both cases are the same, and both approaches are basically elementary, why bother to even mention the differences? In this problem it would make no difference because we have two lots, each lot consisting of fifteen units. In actual practice, you would probably find uneven lot quantities which are dependent upon shop loading, scheduling, and other factors.

As an example, if you are working with an order for fifty units which are to be manufactured in four lots, you may find that instead of scheduling approximately 12.5 units per lot, you have:

First lot	-	5 units
Second lot	-	22 units
Third lot	-	8 units
Fourth lot	-	15 units
TOTAL		50 units

Because of the more realistic broken lot condition you are more apt to experience, it is best to use the second approach when calculating setup per unit, which will give you the average setup per unit charge for that opportunity.

To get a feel for the application of these principles, we will begin with the evaluation of the problem given, and consider the conditions as they arise (Table 7.2).

Which proposal is the least expensive? For proposal A we have a unit cost of $255.00 and an investment of $13,550.00. In proposal B the unit cost is $146.00 for an investment of $20,725.00. With a firm contract of 30 units, the total contract cost comparison is shown in Table 7.3.

Based on this analysis, you would tend to recommend Proposal A as the most economical approach. However, we must also consider the possibility of being awarded the anticipated 150 units following this order of 30 units (total 180 units).

In determining the economics of the proposal using 180 units, it is not necessary to recompute the setup at this time. Since we calculated setup on a per-unit basis the small error percentage would not effect the final outcome (Table 7.4).

Using the anticipated contract quantity, Proposal B becomes more economical. Making a recommendation at this point would depend on whether you are optimistic or pessimistic regarding a follow-on order.

Table 7.2

PROPOSAL A		
RECURRING COST	**CALCULATIONS**	**UNIT COST**
Material		$ 150.00
S. U. / Unit	(See previous example)	10.00
Run Time	$\dfrac{40 \text{ Min} \ (\$60 \ / \ Hr)}{60 \text{ Min} \ / \ Hr}$	40.00
Assembly	$\dfrac{55 \text{ Min} \ (\$60 \ / \ Hr)}{60 \text{ Min} \ / \ Hr}$	55.00
	COST PER UNIT	$ 255.00
Nonrecurring Cost		
Tooling (Co.)	110 Hours ($65 / Hr)	$ 7,150.00
Engineering	80 Hours ($80 / Hr)	6,400.00
Tooling (Vendor)		
	INVESTMENT	$13,550.00

PROPOSAL B		
RECURRING COST	**CALCULATIONS**	**UNIT COST**
Material		$ 50.00
S. U. / Unit	$\dfrac{90 \text{ Min} \ / \ S.U. \ (2 \text{ setups}) \ (\$60 \ / \ Hr)}{60 \text{ Min} \ / \ Hr}$	6.00
Run Time	$\dfrac{55 \text{ Min} \ (\$60 \ / \ Hr)}{60 \text{ Min} \ / \ Hr}$	35.00
Assembly	(Same as Proposal A)	55.00
	COST PER UNIT	$ 146.00
Nonrecurring Cost		
Tooling (Co.)	85 Hours ($65 / Hr)	$ 5,525.00
Engineering	80 Hours ($80 / Hr)	7,200.00
Tooling (Vendor)		8,000.00
	INVESTMENT	$20,725.00

Table 7.3

	PROPOSAL A	PROPOSAL B
TOTAL RECURRING COST	$255.00 (30) = $7650.00	$146.00 (30) = $4380.00
INVESTMENT	$13,550.00	$20,725.00
	Total Cost = $21,200.00	Total Cost = $25,105.00

Cost = $25,105.00 - $21,200.00 = $3,905.00 Favoring "A"

Table 7.4

	PROPOSAL A	PROPOSAL B
TOTAL RECURRING COST	$255.00 (180) = $45,900.00	$146.00 (180) = $26,280.00
INVESTMENT	$13,550.00	$20,725.00
	Total Cost = $59,945.00	Total Cost = $47,005.00

Cost = $59,450.00 - $47,005.00 = $12,445.00 Favoring "B"

If you choose the optimistic approach, you would probably recommend Proposal B, based on future business. The pessimistic view would be to recommend Proposal A because that is the extent of the order in hand.

Is there a compromise? Suppose you recommend Proposal A based on the firm contract of 30 units, and consider Proposal B if the anticipated 150 unit order becomes firm. Before you select this approach, consider once Proposal A is implemented the investment is spent, and analysis becomes an after the fact cost reduction study. Therefore, the cost comparison would appear as follows:

Table 7.5

COMPARATIVE ANALYSIS (150 following 30)

	PROPOSAL A	PROPOSAL B
TOTAL RECURRING COST		
(Based on 150)	$38,250.00	$21.900.00
INVESTMENT	None	$20,725.00
TOTAL COST	$38,250.00	$42,625.00

COST = ($42,625.00 - $38,250.00) = $4,375.00 Favoring "A"

This compromise would not help in making a no risk decision because the analysis shows that once you have produced Proposal A, it would be uneconomical to invest in the redesign for an additional quantity of 150 units.

PROBLEM EXAMPLE SUMMARY

Having all the pertinent cost information relating to a study does not necessarily mean a clean-cut recommendation can be made favoring the least expensive approach. Also, the order quantity should relate to the most economical design configuration and production approach in selecting alternate approaches.

Reviewing the condition of the study, we find:
a. Recommending Proposal A would assure us of the most economical approach for the firm order for 30 units, but would be relatively uneconomical if the follow-on award of 150 additional units were ordered.

b. Proposal B represents the least expensive approach for the total 180 units. However, if the follow-on award did not materialize, we have chosen the expensive approach for the 30 unit order.

c. Selecting Proposal A for the 30 unit contract and recommending a design change to Proposal B if the anticipated 150 unit contract becomes firm represents the most expensive approach of all options considered.

Since we have stipulated that both proposals are technically equal, the choice is based on cost and investment risk.

Although this is an academic problem designed to simulate these conditions, it is by no means uncommon to Value Engineers. An easy out sometimes sought by Value Engineers is reflected in the following statement:

Since Value Engineering is not charged with the responsibility for making the design selection decision, the Value Engineer's job ends with the presentation of the facts ...

This is partially true. The Value Engineer normally does not have the implementation decision, it is the design engineer's responsibility. However, the Value Engineer must recommend the best approach based on facts which may not be readily apparent to the design engineer. This does not say that the design engineer must accept the Value Engineer's recommendation, but it also does not excuse the Value Engineer from a responsibility inherent to his position as an adviser.

Now that we have closed all the nonevaluation avenues leading to a conclusion of this problem, we can return to the analysis to determine some basis for evaluating the most economical proposal.

BREAK-EVEN ANALYSIS

The term "break-even" refers to that point where the revenues received equal the invested expenses to generate those revenues. In business management it is used to analyze return on investment (ROI), return on assets (ROA), when profit is generated, and other analysis techniques.

To the Value Engineer, break-even analysis will establish when, in terms of quantity produced, one design option is economically equal to another design approach. To program management, these data are considered more useful than the total cost effect of the alternates being considered.

In commercial and industrial markets, the annual production quantity is a business objective. Once established, this sales goal represents the basis for the type of tooling used, the amount of capital to be invested, market share, profit, and all the other financial relationships which pivot about the product itself.

With the exception of high volume expendables, federal government contractors cannot really determine their annual production quantity. The number of units to be built are directly dependent on specific contracts with government agencies that spell out the amount of deliverable units. Since the users (the government) of these products represent a very limited market, the manufacturer has little control over the annual production rates. Any consideration of annual production quantities in the cases which include firm plus potential contracts must be treated as a variable rather than a fixed production quota. This has a direct effect on the product's configuration and production approach. To cite an example: the use of Hybred and LSI circuits or large complex integral castings are economical, provided there are sufficient production quantities to absorb the higher development investments required.

Expanding on the problem being evaluated, we can approximate and determine if, and when, a break-even point exists by constructing a simple amortization chart.

Recalling the definitions discussed, recurring costs in this example are considered a continuous fixed charge, and are incurred with each item produced. In addition, if we amortize the non-recurring costs, each item would equally share the invested expenses necessary to affect production. Therefore, the larger the production quantity, the smaller the non-recurring cost per item. We will once again discount the manufacturing setup adjustment, and accept the small percentage of error (since we treat both proposals the same) in favor of exploring the principals involved in arriving at a solution (Table 7.6).

As this analysis indicates, Proposal B becomes less expensive somewhere between the 65th and the 70th unit. If we consider implementing Proposal A for the firm 30 unit order, then changing to Proposal B if the anticipated contract becomes firm, we would need a contract quantity slightly less than 200 to break-even. This is shown by comparing the recurring plus amortized non-recurring costs in Proposal B, to the recurring cost of Proposal A. (Remember, the non-recurring cost in Proposal A would have been expended).

Since we are specifically looking for that quantity where one proposal is economically equal to its alternate(s), we can now develop an equation to determine that point, using the principle of the amortization chart. Assuming that a point of equivalency does exist, we compare design proposals by setting one proposal equal to its alternate(s) and solving for the break-even, or crossover, point(s). To reduce the expressions used in the equation, the following symbols are applicable:

N_A = Non-recurring cost of Proposal A

R_A = Recurring cost of Proposal A

N_B = Non-recurring cost of Proposal B

R_B = Recurring cost of Proposal B

X = Break-even or crossover point

Table 7.7

AMORTIZATION CHART

PROPOSAL A

QTY.	NONRECURRING COST / UNIT	RECURRING COST / UNIT	TOTAL UNIT COST
1	13,550.00	255.00	13,805.00
2	6,775.00	255.00	7,030.00
5	2,710.00	255.00	2,965.00
10	1,350.00	255.00	1,610.00
50	271.00	255.00	526.00
65	208.50	255.00	463.50
70	193.60	255.00	448.60
100	135.50	255.00	390.50
150	90.30	255.00	345.30
200	67.80	255.00	322.80

PROPOSAL B

QTY.	NONRECURRING COST / UNIT	RECURRING COST / UNIT	TOTAL UNIT COST
1	20,725.00	146.00	20,871.00
2	10,362.50	146.00	10,508.50
5	4,145.00	146.00	4,291.00
10	2,072.50	146.00	2,218.50
50	414.50	146.00	560.50
65	318.00	146.00	464.00
70	296.10	146.00	442.10
100	207.30	146.00	353.30
150	138.20	146.00	284.42
200	103.70	146.00	249.70

At the Break Even Point (BEP)

$$N_A + R_A (X) = N_B + R_B (X)$$

Solving for X,

$$(R_A - R_B) X = N_B - N_A \text{ or } X = \frac{N_B - N_A}{R_A - R_B?}$$

Which reduces to:

$$X = \frac{\Delta N}{\Delta R} \text{ for the 'BEFORE THE FACT' studies.}$$

Applying the given information cited in the problem, and determining the BEP:

Given:

$$N_A = \$13,550.00 \qquad\qquad N_B = \$20,725.00$$

$$R_A = \quad 225.00 \qquad\qquad R_B = \quad 146.00$$

$$X = \frac{20,725.00 - 13,550.00}{(225.00 - 146.00)} = \frac{7,175.00}{109.00}$$

$$X = 65.8 \text{ or } 66 \text{ units}$$

Solving for the BEP where it is proposed to redesign if the additional 150 units order is awarded, we do not include the non-recurring cost of the existing design (Proposal A) in the analysis because we assume the funds were spent.

It could be argued that the proposed design change must also account for the invested non-recurring cost in addition to the new implementation charges by stating:

Although it is true that the non-recurring cost necessary to produce the existing design has been spent, the proposed design will require additional investments to implement. Therefore, that design change must carry the invested expenses in addition to its own, in order to determine the total investment required.

However, the mathematical solution to the break-even point considers this condition in its equation:

$$X = \frac{(NB = NA) - NA}{R_A - R_B} \quad \text{or} \quad \frac{2{,}072.50 + 1{,}355.00) - 1{,}355.00}{(25.50 - 14.60)}$$

$$X = \frac{NB}{R} \text{ For "AFTER THE FACT" studies or } X = \frac{2{,}072.5}{10.90}$$

X = 190.1 or 191 units

If X ≥ 1, a BEP exists
If x ≤ 0, no BEP exists

THE BREAK-EVEN CURVE

We have seen that the break-even point represents the quantity or point where the alternates considered are economically equal. By examining the conditions immediately prior to and after this point, we also know that the BEP represents the point where the economic conditions of the alternates change. However, what is the relationship of the alternates to this change, the cost differential at any given unit, the slope characteristics? Even with two alternates this information is difficult to determine. With three, four, or more alternates the problem is compounded and the task of determining their interrelationships using only the break-even points becomes difficult.

Displaying these relationships graphically will simplify the analysis. This graphical method of evaluation is called the break-even curve. Plotting the curve presents a pictorial illustration of the amortization chart previously developed.

In Value Engineering we use the break-even curve to show that point in the contract where one method of fabrication becomes less costly than the other. Sales and profit are not considered in these analyses, only the cost to produce the design. The curve at a first glance appears to differ from the conventional approach, but the mechanics are similar.

This form of the curve is generally plotted on a 2 by 3 cycle logarithmic graph paper. The log scales are especially useful because high tooling, engineering, development, and other non-recurring charges make compression of the vertical (ordinate) scales desirable. Large quantities of units make it necessary to compress the horizontal (abscissa) scale. Using this scale also permits easy reading of the intermediate points in the areas of rapid change. Also, an experience factor or learning curve can be incorporated on the same graph since it is a logarithmic function.

The curve itself plots cost per unit against quantity of units, with the non-recurring or invested costs amortized over the quantity indicated. Superimposing two, three or any number of alternate designs will show all the break-even points. Cost differences of one design over another can be quickly determined from the graph, making it easier to include cost into design decisions (Figures 7.1 and 7.2). Using this approach, any point (P) on the curve would equal

$$P = \frac{NR_Q}{Q} + R$$

The break-even curve most commonly used in financial analysis is based on the same principle adapted for alternate design analysis in Value Engineering. However, the approach is slightly different. This approach analyzes the product with the sales price using rectangular coordinate graph paper. The BEP occurs somewhere prior to the total annual production quantity. Since the total production is a fixed quantity, the recurring cost of each unit is treated as cumulative cost and plotted against the number of units to be produced. Therefore, the invested non-recurring costs are considered fixed, rather than being amortized into the unit cost, and the recurring costs are now considered as variables. Any point (P) on the curve would equal $P = NR + R(Q)$. A simple break-even curve illustrating these principles appears in Figure 7.3.

Note that the break-even or crossover in Figure 7.3 considers the production cost with respect to the sales forecast; not the alternate method approach used in Value Engineering to determine which design approach to employ. However, this approach also lends itself to alternate design evaluation. One advantage of this system is the relative ease of plotting and illustrating the recurring and non-recurring costs as well as those items considered fixed variables.

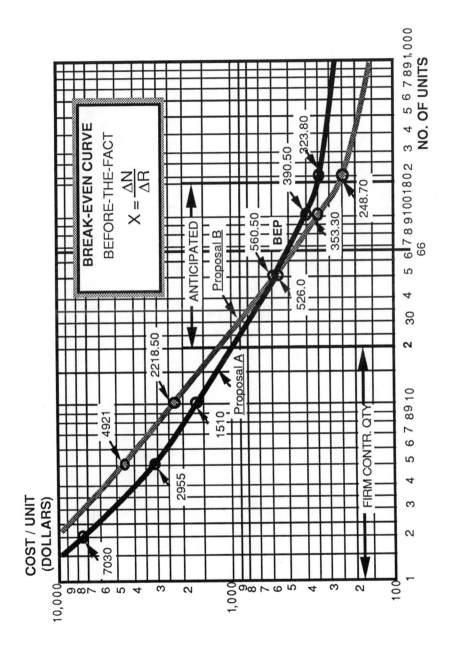

Figure 7.1

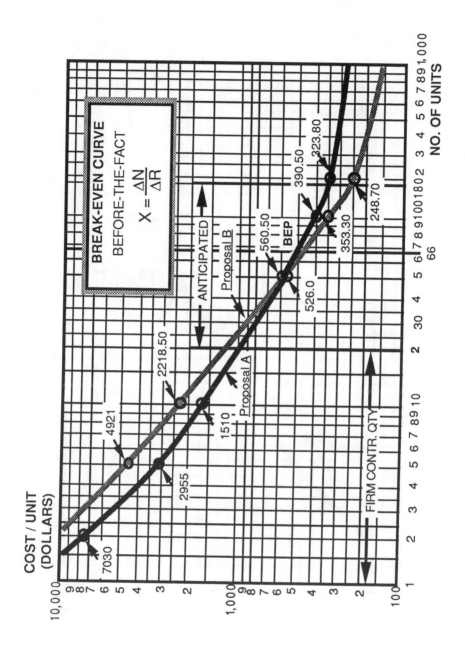

Figure 7.2

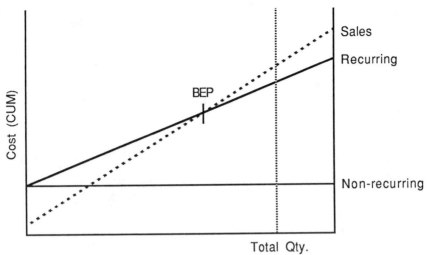

Figure 7.3

As seen in Figure 7.4, the non-recurring costs, classified as "fixed," are a constant shown as a horizontal line. The recurring costs, which are variables, are cumulative and are a direct function of quantity. Other charges which are "fixed" behave as variable expenses because they are calculated as a percentage of another expense. Some examples are engineering liason, tool maintenance, overhead, taxes, and G & A.

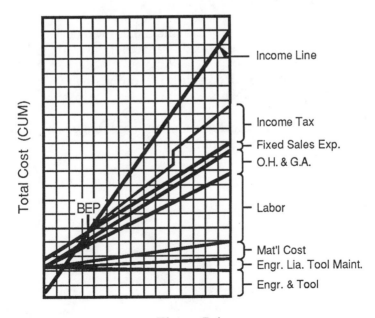

Figure 7.4

We can also use this break-even approach to our requirements in making comparative analysis of two or more design approaches; either in the "before the fact" (Figure 7.5) or "after the fact" (Figure 7.6) examples. Using the conditions of the problem we have been working with, the break-even curve would appear as see in Figures 7.5 and 7.6.

There are common characteristics and conditions evident regardless of which approach is used.

1. In comparing alternates, a break-even point exists if the difference in recurring cost favors one approach, and the non-recurring favors the other(s). If the difference in recurring and non-recurring costs both favor one approach, there is no break-even point.

2. If a BEP exists it will favor the alternate with the lowest recurring cost (or highest non-recurring cost).

$$\text{If } x \geq 1, \text{ a BEP exists}$$

$$\text{If } x < 0, \text{ no BEP exists}$$

CHAPTER 7 QUESTIONS

To test your understanding of the break-even concept, you should be able to answer the following questions:

1. With respect to any point (P) on the break-even curve, how does amortizing nonrecurring costs differ from them as fixed costs?

2. Would increasing or decreasing the order quantity affect the break-even point? Explain.

3. How many potential break-even points are there when evaluating 3 proposals; and 4 proposals?

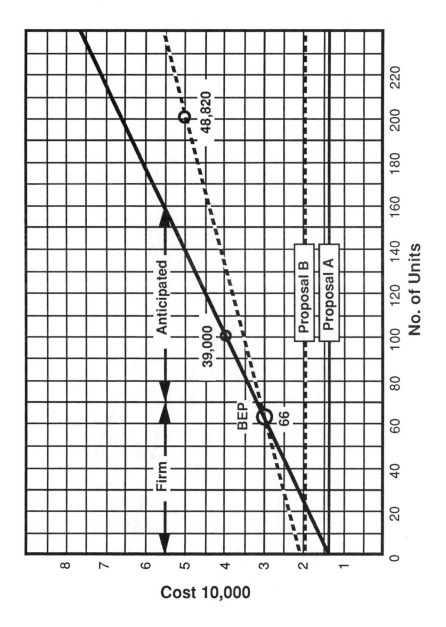

Figure 7.5

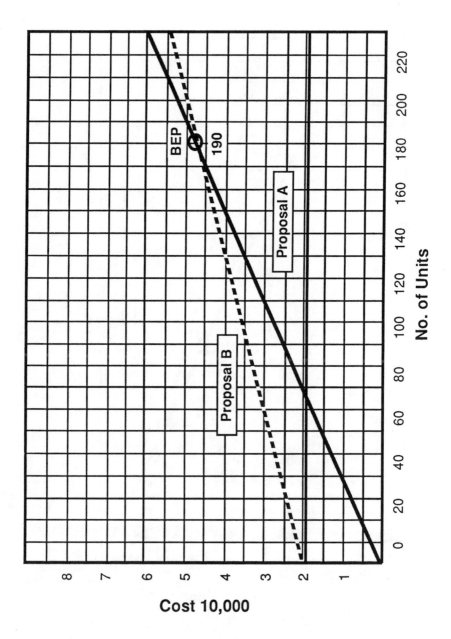

Figure 7.6

7-22

Chapter 8

THE EXPERIENCE CURVE

INTRODUCTION

Experience curves, sometimes called "learning," "cost improvement," and "industrial curves," offer a means of predicting the impact of future improvements on successive production lots. The concept of experience curves is based on the statistical fact that whenever a production quantity doubles, there is a constant rate of improvement in the time (or cost) to produce that product. The techniques have applicability to other manufacturing and design efforts in the areas of cost control, cost projection, procurement, planning, scheduling, budgeting, and estimating functions. The application of experience curves for Value Engineering will focus on studies usually encountered in the analysis to determine the most economical design approach in high volume production situations. The principal use of experience curves in Value Engineering is to analyze the economic effects of alternate designs, especially if the new design will take the place of one currently in production.

Break-even analysis determines when the nonrecurring cost, or investment payback period will occur. The experience curve can predict when the rate of improvement of a new design will overtake an existing design, making it more economically attractive. Experience curves can also be used to predict labor cost, schedule production, analyze material costs (Economic Order Quantities), and determine the economics of make or buy.

BACKGROUND

T. P. Wright is credited with advancing the theory of improvement or experience curves in a 1936 paper published in the *Journal of Aeronautical Sciences*. Wright identified five important elements which determine airplane structural costs. Excluding avionics, these elements still hold true today.

1. Design complexity factors, including material used
2. Tooling and its adaptability to the design
3. The amount of engineering changes after release
4. The size and weight of the aircraft
5. The number of aircraft produced

During World War II, aircraft manufacturers discovered that as their unskilled workers gained experience, the time and cost to produce aircraft decreased following the principles described by Wright. They also found, with additional statistical tools, that production costs and schedules could be predicted.

A later analysis by the Air Material Command found that the average improvement rate (AIR) of the aircraft industry during WW II was 79.7%. Thereafter, the "Wright 80% airplane curve" became the baseline for that and related industry. A fallacy in using this curve as a standard is that each company, product, component, assembly, etc., has unique improvement rate characteristics.

The data that were used to arrive at the 80% curve clearly show variations among companies, type of aircraft, and even the same aircraft produced by one company.

Company	Type of Aircraft	Improvement Curve
Boeing-Wichita	(first 900 B-29's)	71.8%
Boeing-Wichita	(last 800 B-29's)	69.5%
Boeing-Renton	(first 400 B-29's)	80.5%
Boeing-Renton	(last 700 B-29's)	79.0%
Lockheed-Burbank	(B-17)	65.3%
Douglas-Long Beach	(first 1000 B-17's)	77.4%
Convair-Fort Worth	(first 1000 B-24's)	76.4%
Douglas-Tulsa	(B-24E)	75.0%
Ford-Willow Run	(B-24)	70.8%
North American-Dallas	(B-24)	75.0%
Beech-Wichita	(AT-10)	76.7%
North American-Dallas	(AT-6)	98.0%
Republic-Farmingdale	(P-47N)	89.0%

Studies made since the close of the second World War have shown similar variations in the curve percentages for individual aircraft. A study of 12 fighter planes revealed percentages ranging from 67% to 91%. Eleven post World War II Bombers have shown direct labor improvement curves with percentages varying from 63% to 84%.

There are many factors that affect an improvement curve. Each company and product is different, and therefore, each will have different rates of improvement. In manufacturing the same item some companies may show very steep percentage improvement curves such as 70% while other companies will show an improvement curve of 95%. There are many reasons for this.

Some companies are more efficient and better managed than others. Others bring to a specific contract or production run accumulated experience from other similar production which assists them in developing efficient methods at the beginning of a job.

The validity of experience curves has since been tested through thousands of studies based on actual case histories involving the broad spectrum of manufactured goods. The theory holds that a statistical relationship develops, indicating that as the number of production units doubles, the cumulative average hours per unit will reduce at a constant rate. This rate will vary between operation, job, products, and companies, but once determined will represent the key to predicting and developing trends in production costs. Keep in mind that the experience curve approach is not a panacea. It is a tool, a statistical device, requiring judgment in its use in order to be of value.

Experience curves follow a mathematical pattern in which some consistent percent reduction is achieved each time the quantity is doubled. In each case, the specific percentage is identified as soon as data on two different quantities are determined. The experience curve can be expressed mathematically in a number of forms. One such expression is as follows:

$$Y = AX^b$$

Y = cost of the Nth unit (hours or dollars)
A = cost of the 1st unit $(x - 1)$
b = "slope" parameter where:

$$b = \frac{\log\left(\frac{S(\%)}{100}\right)}{.301030}$$

This chapter deals principally with the graphical, rather than the mathematical approach to experience curves, for several reasons.

1. Although the math formula is exacting, the answer must be interpreted with seasoned judgment to be useful.

2. A graphical display will illustrate trends, which in experience curves is more important than single point answers.

3. Once the general principal is understood, a sheet of 2 x 3 log-log graph paper and a straight edge are all that are needed to construct and solve 90% of the experience curve problems well within acceptable accuracy limits.

4. If greater accuracy is required, there are a number of computer software programs available to mathematically and graphically display the experience curves.

Let us begin by applying the principal of experience curves.

THE CUMULATIVE AVERAGE

As an example, in a particular production run it has been determined that as the number of units produced doubles, the cumulative average costs per unit decreases by 20%. This is called an 80% slope as seen below. The first production unit establishes the original cost. The average cost of the first two units in this case is 80% of the first. The average cost of the first four units is 80% of the first two, or 64% of the first unit. The average cost of the first eight units is 80% of the first four, or 51% of the first, and so on. Plotting these data on rectangular coordinates, it can be seen that the slope assumes the characteristics of a hyperbola (see Figure 8.1).

80% SLOPE

Unit No.	Unit Cum. Avg.	Cumulative Total
1	100	100
2	80	160
4	64	256
8	51	408
16	41	656
32	33	1056
64	26	1664

This can be expressed as an arithmetic progression, plotted as a straight line on a logarithmic scale (see Figure 8.2). As previously discussed, the graphical rather than mathematical approach will be used in this section. Plotting the given information on a 2 x 3 log-log paper, the problem can be quickly illustrated and solved using this approach (see Figure 8.2).

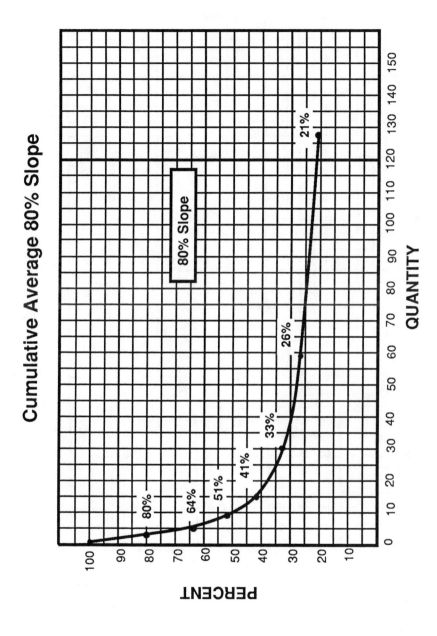

Figure 8.1

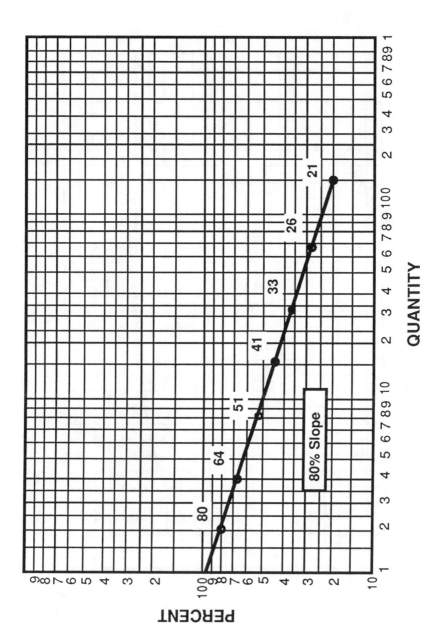

Figure 8.2

8-6

PROBLEM: The cost of the first production unit is 300 hours; using an 80% slope, what would the cumulative average of the 85th unit be? (See Figure 8.3).

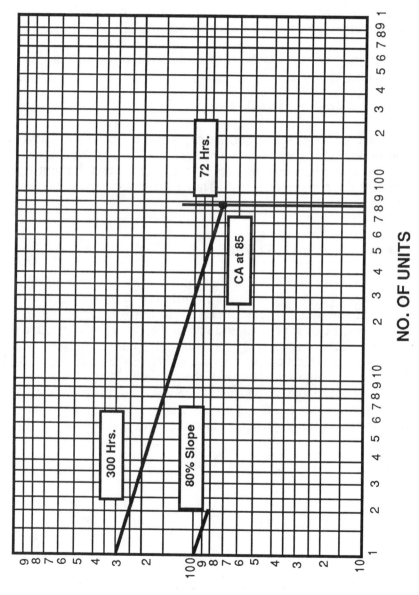

Figure 8.3

THE UNIT VALUE

In developing the experience curve, it is sometimes beneficial to know the unit cost of a particular item in production. Since the experience curve is based on decreasing production costs, the unit cost of a specific production quantity will always be less than its cumulative average. There are two exceptions to this rule which will become more apparent as the curve develops:

    a. at the first unit, where of course, there is no cumulative average, and

    b. if the slope used is 100%.

The rate of regression (or slope) of the unit cost curve is proportional to its cumulative average. As the slope decreases, the linear distance between the cumulative average and the unit value increases for a given quantity. Therefore, it too can be calculated and plotted on the log-log graph.

EXPONENT OF THE SLOPE

The slope of the curve can be determined graphically by using any two given points from the cumulative average curve and constructing a right triangle formed by the horizontal grid line of the smaller quantity, the vertical grid line of the greater quantity, and the portion of the curve lying between the chosen points. The measurement of the slope can be established as the ratio of the length of the vertical leg to the length of the horizontal leg of the triangle. By taking advantage of the triangle constructed, in which the slope represents the hypotenuse of a right triangle, we can establish that the exponent of the slope equals the tangent of that angle.

$$E = \text{Tangent } \phi = \frac{\text{Vertical Length}}{\text{Horizontal Length}}$$

For an example, see Figure 8.4.

Graphical Development of Exponent

In Figure 8.4, side BC of the triangle measures 3-7/32 inches, side AB measures 10 inches, and the ratio equals 0.3219 approximately. In actual practice, it is not necessary to construct this triangle as it is formed by the grids of the graph and the curve previously constructed.

The problem is further simplified by working with 11 by 17, 2 by 3 cycle, log-log graph paper by choosing two points from the curve which are separated by two complete cycles. As each cycle is five inches in length, this method will always produce a triangle with side AB equal to 10 inches. The ratio is then quickly determined by measuring side BC only, converting from fraction to decimal equivalent, and moving the decimal one place to the left.

The value determined above is known as "the exponent of the slope of the curve" and is used in solution by formulas of the problems involving the curve. The exponent table will also translate the exponent solved to the slope of the curve.

NOTES

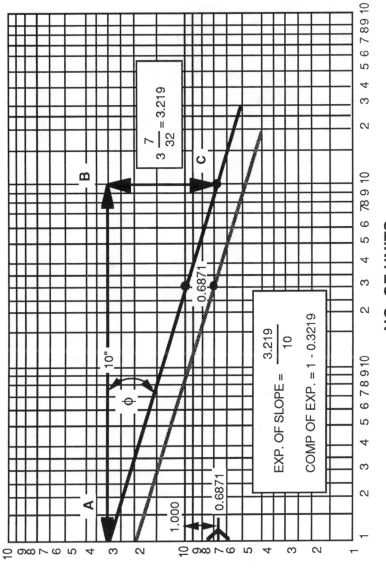

Figure 8.4

COMPLEMENT OF EXPONENT -- ITS USE

The next step is to establish a method of measuring the distance which separates the unit curve from the cumulative average curve at any given quantity. First the value of the complement of the exponent (CE) is determined. In this example (see Figure 8.4), it is 1.000 minus 0.3219, or 0.6781. This is converted to linear units by measuring the vertical distance from the top of the first cycle on the log-log graph, which is expressed as 1.0, to the horizontal grid line representing 0.6781. This distance below the cumulative average curve, laid off on one of the vertical grid lines, will determine one point of the unit curve. The unit curve, with the exception of smaller quantities, can now be drawn through the derived point as a straight line parallel to the cumulative average curve.

We can summarize the conditions established thus far in the form shown below. With this information and the correct data, almost all "experience curve" type problems can be solved graphically.

SYMBOLS	DEFINITIONS
E, Exponent:	Defines the slope of the curve.
CE, Complement of Exponent:	Used to determine linear distance between CA and U. Difference between CA and U for a given quantity.
CA, Cumulative Averages:	The average value of one unit in a specific quantity.
U, Unit (cost) Value:	The value of a specific unit.

$$E = TAN\ \Phi = \frac{VERT}{HOR}, \text{ or } 1.000 - CE$$

$$CE = \frac{U}{CA}, \text{ or } 1.000 - E$$

Table 8.1

EXPONENT TABLE

Slope	Exponent	Slope	Exponent
60%	0.7369664	80%	0.3219280
61	0.7131182	81	0.3040062
62	0.6896588	82	0.2863036
63	0.6665747	83	0.2688170
64	0.6438560	84	0.2515397
65%	0.6214895	85%	0.2344650
66	0.5994618	86	0.2175929
67	0.5777663	87	0.2009135
68	0.5563930	88	0.1844234
69	0.5353320	89	0.1681227
70%	0.5145732	90%	0.1520014
71	0.4941102	91	0.1360628
72	0.4739295	92	0.1202969
73	0.4540311	93	0.1046972
74	0.4344018	94	0.0892668
75%	0.4150383	95%	0.0739992
76	0.3959273	96	0.0588944
77	0.3770687	97	0.0439457
78	0.3584526	98	0.0291465
79	0.3400757	99	0.0144968

CORRECTING FOR THE UNIT VALUE, GRAPHICALLY

Determining the accuracy of the relationship between the unit value and cumulative average at any given unit can be approximated. An approved method of graphical "correction" has been developed which accepts the small degree of error (no greater than the interpreted reading of values on the graph) for speed in reading the graph.

Once the complement of the exponent has been determined, a line parallel to the cumulative average is drawn extending to the first unit. At the point where the unit value line intersects the "half" units, draw a horizontal line to the next full unit. (For example, at 1-1/2 units construct a horizontal line to 2 units; at 2-1/2 move horizontally to 3; at 3-1/2 move horizontally to 4, etc.) Then, starting with the intersection of the first unit, draw the unit value curve connecting the points established.

As noted in Figure 8.5, it is only necessary to determine the corrected unit curve for the first five units. From that point, blend the line from the 5th unit to the 30th and consider the unit curve parallel to the cumulative average beyond unit number 30.

APPLICATION OF THE EXPERIENCE CURVE

Determining data normally found on the experience curve can be accomplished if any two bits of comparable information are given. The combination of this given information could be in the form of:

1. a cumulative average value and its slope

2. a unit value and its slope

3. two cumulative average points

4. two unit values

5. a cumulative average and unit value for a given quantity

NOTES

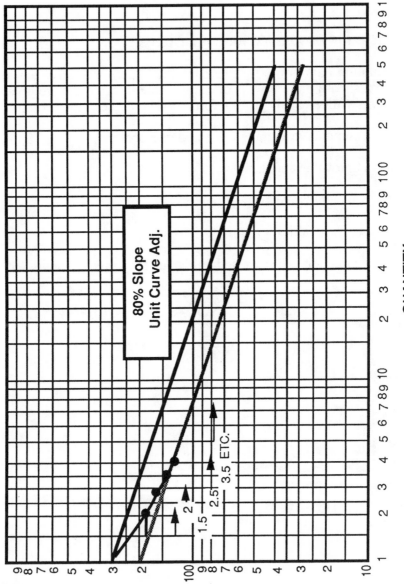

Figure 8.5

PROBLEM EXAMPLES

Using the information given, solve the following problems graphically.

<u>Problem No. 1</u> (see Figure 8.6)

As a Value Engineer in a component manufacturing company, you are required to estimate the cumulative average (CA) labor hours per unit for an order involving 150 units. Since production has started, you established that at the current 40 units the CA is eight hours. Through historical records, it was also established that the reduction in labor followed a slope of 80%.

In addition to the CA at 150, also determine the:

(a) cost of the first unit

(b) unit cost of the 40th unit

(c) units cost of the 150th unit

<u>Problem No.2</u>

In sampling a production run, you find that the 100th unit you have chosen has a CA of 4.5 hours and a unit value (U) of 2.6 hours.

From the information given, determine:

(a) the slope of the experience curve

(b) the CA and unit hours at

    (1) 2nd unit (use corrected value)
    (2) 50th unit
    (3) 110th unit

<u>Problem No. 3</u>

Given: CA at 40 = 8.00 hours

    U at 40 = 4.67

Find: Slope

    Unit cost at 2nd corrected.

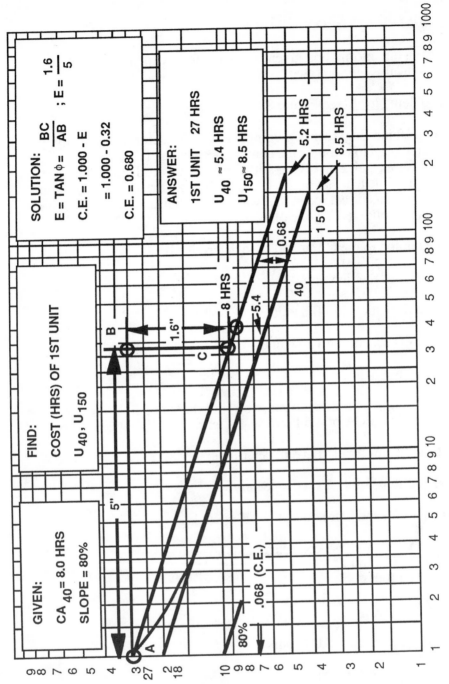

Figure 8.6

8-16

PROBLEM EXAMPLE SOLUTIONS

Problem No. 1 (see Figure 8.6)
Given: Cumulative average (CA) at 40 = 8.00 hours.

Find: Unit cost -

Solution No.1

1. Plot point on graph

2. Draw 80% curve through point

3. Construct
   NOTE: Use 5 inches as assumption. (PT AB)

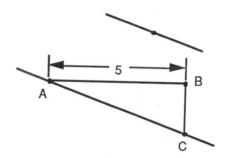

4. (E) = Exponent $= \dfrac{\text{Vert}}{\text{Hor}} = \dfrac{BC}{AB} = \dfrac{1.6}{5}$

   $= 0.32$

5. Comp. of Exp. = (CE) $= \dfrac{U}{CA}$ or

   (CE) = 1.000 - E

   $= 1.000 - 0.32 = .68$

6.

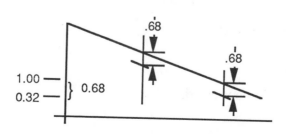

Problem No.2

Given: CA at 100 unit = 4.5

U at 100 unit = 2.6

Find: Slope

Solution No.2

$$CE = \frac{U}{CA} = \frac{2.6}{4.5} = 0.577$$

$$E = \frac{Vert}{Hor} \text{ or } 1.000 - 0.577 = 0.423$$

(0.423 (book) = approximately 75%)

(or Plot)

$$(E) \ 0.423 = \frac{Vert}{(assume \ 4") \ Hor} = Vert$$

$$= 0.423(4) = 1.692$$

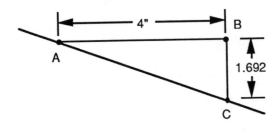

Problem No.3

Given:
CA at 40 = 8.00 hours

U at 40 = 4.67

Find: Slope

Unit cost at 2nd corrected.

Solution No.3

$$CE = \frac{U}{CA} = \frac{4.67}{8.00} = 0.585$$

$$E = 1.000 - 0.585 = 0.415$$

$$E = (Tan) = \frac{Vert}{Hor} \text{ (assume 4" Hor)}$$

$$E = 0.415 = \frac{Vert}{4}$$

Vert. = 4(0.415) = 1.66 inches

Chapter 9

THE EXECUTION PHASE

Now that the fun and excitement of the speculation and planning phases come to an end, the ideas and concepts developed by the freewheeling "anything is possible" approach must be analyzed under the harsh light of reality. The speculations must now be proven; plans must be worked out. The focus of the team shifts from divergent to convergent thinking. It is in this phase that the potential solutions previously selected are analyzed for technical feasibility, economic risk, timing, and market acceptability. Once again, the value of interdisciplinary task teams surfaces as knowledgeable team members contribute their expertise to resolving the variety of issues necessary to "package" a successful solution.

The concepts representing the proposed solutions must be confirmed and refined. Physical tests may be performed on product models to validate technical assumptions. Quotes should be solicited to verify the cost of purchased materials. Shop estimates should be gathered and analyzed to confirm manufacturing approaches, labor costs, and tooling expenses. Schedules and priorities should be resolved to insure the availability of resources and many other details attended to that require resolution and approval prior to implementation.

The execution phase is the most critical in Value Engineering. It is the inattention to this difficult work that causes many VE proposals and programs to fall short of implementation success. It is the inability to convert potential cost improvements to reality that has resulted in management disillusionment called "paper savings."

Discouragement is the major factor to be overcome by the task team during the execution phase. Many of the ideas that looked excellent in speculation and promising in planning will develop "holes" as they stand the feasibility test. Discouragement mounts as the investigating task team members encounter apathy, or even antagonism by those people who are responsible for, or affected by, the implementation of the VE teams proposals. Many will have built-in biases and resistance to change developed over many years of "protecting their turf." However, it is part of the Value Engineer's job to sell them and solicit their help in a nonthreatening, supportive manner.

MULTIPLE DEVELOPMENT

The concept of concurrent, multiple development should be maintained throughout the entire study. When final recommendations are presented, management should have several options from which to choose. There are a number of reasons supporting this approach.

1. Developing at least three concurrent proposals for implementation reduces the chances of a total loss if a single track approach should encounter a problem which cannot be effectively resolved. As the three approaches move through their initial milestones and pass through the critical "gates" the parallel development options can be dropped or set aside. However, if a problem should develop with the preferred solution, the next option or a combination of approaches and features is available as a fall back position.

2. Presenting three (or more) options to the decision makers may bring out selection factors which were unavailable to the VE team during the information or study phase. This could change the option priorities. Also, involving those managers in the selection process gives them a vested sense of ownership in the successful outcome of the proposed solutions.

3. Allowing for some flexibility by the implementation authority outside of the VE task team also builds involvement and commitment by those affected. Many will resist changes because they have not been included in the development of the solutions. As such, they may look upon themselves as "outsiders." Bringing them into the process by keeping some approaches open will gain support for the principal ideas. Examples include: asking the manufacturing people for their ideas on processing the product; engineering for the best technical option; purchasing to search for the most responsive supplier; quality to point out potential problem areas; etc.

ORGANIZATION AND ANALYSIS

Although it may appear contradictory to the creative process, there are some advantages to formatting the conclusions of the study in some standard manner. Use of a standard format has several advantages.

1. The forms act as a check list to insure that all the important issues were addressed.

2. Presenting a standard study format to the approval authority makes analysis easier in their decision-making process.

3. Questions arising from the approval board can be recorded as issues to be addressed on the next similar study.

4. A professional format helps organize and "sell" the proposal. This will be explored further in the next chapter.

Several forms which may be useful in preparing proposals are included at the end of the chapter.

A major disadvantage to consider in presenting a standard study format is that a form cannot possibly encompass the wide variety of subjects for a Value Engineering study. To attempt to do so would make the forms much too complex for any one application. Don't rely on the form to carry the study. Forms are tools, not end products. As discussed in earlier chapters, VE has been effectively applied to equipment, facilities, capital, operations, software, new product development, business planning, as well as the classic "after the fact" product cost reduction. Over thirty-five years of Value Engineering practices have proven that the disciplines as described in previous chapters are equally effective across a broad market spectrum and study issue.

As an example of one approach to the execution phase, the forms illustrated in this chapter will favor the product cost reduction opportunities in Value Engineering.

As all the information is brought together to document and justify the VE proposals, an outline is recommended to help organize the report (see pages 9-5 and 9-6). The "key questions" and "check list" cover the most common questions asked by management. The answers should be incorporated in the body of the report.

Figure 9.1 is a summary of the study and the results. The objective of the study should be restated. If the objective changed during the course of the investigation, it should be noted. As an example, if the objective was to "reduce the product cost," but the team discovered a new product idea which recommends doing away with the original product, the recommendation should be written to justify deviating from the original objective. Summary results should identify the potential accomplishments of the recommended proposals. How to achieve those results, and any shortcomings, risks, requirements, or additional tests should be specified in the body of the report. It is also important to recognize the team participants and any contributions coming from outside the team structure.

The "Value Engineering Analysis" form (Figure 9.2) compares the current design with the recommended alternative. If more than one alternative is considered, additional pages of this and other related information sheets can be added.

The axiom "a picture is worth a thousand words" is especially true in preparing the Value Engineering proposal. Good illustrations that highlight the area of change, along with a well documented report, add to the credibility of the proposal. The bottom of the form brings all entries to the cost effects of the proposal. In the summary box, the "proposed effectivity point" is the first unit in a production lot that incorporates the proposed changes. This is not the break-even point. The effectivity point (or unit) considers committed production quantities, purchase orders placed, units in inventory, and other associated material that must be either depleted or scrapped before the proposed change can be put into effect. Incidentally, this is one reason why "before the fact" Value Engineering is more effective than product cost reduction.

The break-even analysis box provides for up to three alternate proposals compared to each other and the current design. It is highly recommended that break-even curves accompany the report (see Chapter 7). The curves not only illustrate the dynamics occurring before and after the break-even point, but also quickly answer many "what if..." questions that may come up during proposal review.

The "comparison to present method" form (Figure 9.3) identifies the specific components affected by the alternate approach being considered. Note that the advantages as well as the disadvantages are identified.

The nonrecurring costs represent the investment required to implement the suggested approach. Note also that the recurring costs are separated from investment. This is to allow for the break-even analysis of the alternative with the current design (see Chapter 7).

Figures 9.4 and 9.5 are narrative pages to explain the analysis and broaden the information contained in the cover page (Figure 9.1). However, "tests and evaluation" (Figure 9.5) is shown separately, to add emphasis to the qualification testing that may be required to validate the conclusions of the study. As in the previous report pages, additional sheets, graphs, prints, illustrations, etc., may be added to the report as required.

The concluding point is to emphasize that the execution phase must be tested with as much depth and analysis as any serious business venture in the company. Unlike many "suggestions" programs, the VE proposal must be complete upon presentation for a decision. Only in this way can Value Engineering command the respect and position it deserves as an effective management discipline.

Execution Phase

Purpose:

    a. To establish a program of investigation for study of alternative methods selected in the planning phase
    b. To assess the technical feasibility of the alternate methods
    c. To acquire additional information concerning the alternate methods
    d. To test market acceptability of the proposed solutions

Techniques:

    a. Use good human relations
    b. Spend the company's money as you would your own
    c. Work on specifics not generalities
    d. Plan to use:
        1. Standards
        2. Specialty processes
        3. Specialty products and materials
    e. Test all assumptions

Key Questions:

    a. Will the alternate methods satisfy all requirements?
    b. Are there any open issues requiring resolution before implementation?
    c. Are reliability requirements met by the alternatives?
    d. Are the alternatives compatible with the system of which it is a part?
    e. Are safety requirements met by the alternatives?
    f. Do the alternatives improve or at least not adversely affect their maintainability characteristics or those of the system of which they are a part?

g. Do the alternatives account for product interchangeability, inventory costs, spares, logistics, distribution, government regulations, and other support requirements?

h. Will the successful implementation of alternatives support management's commitment to the business plan?

CHAPTER 9 QUESTIONS

1. What is the purpose of the Execution Phase?

2. True or False: to keep the cost of development down it is advisable to select the best proposal and put all resources into its implementation (explain).

3. True or False: it is most important that all forms are properly filled out to insure that key issues have been addressed (explain).

VALUE ENGINEERING ANALYSIS

SUBJECT: PROPOSAL NO.:

OBJECTIVE OF THE STUDY: DATE:

SUMMARY RESULTS:

CONCLUSIONS

VALUE ENGINEERING TASK TEAM

NAME	POSITION	PHONE NO.

Figure 9.1

VALUE ENGINEERING / ANALYSIS

Subject:			Proposal No.:	
Component No.	Name:		Function(s):	
Product	Qty. per Device:		Marketing Forecast:	Date:

PRESENT (Show Sketches):

PROPOSED (Show Sketches):
ALTERNATE: _____

NON-RECURRING COSTS			COST	MATERIAL	LABOR & BURDEN	NON-RECUR. UNIT COSTS	TOTAL COST PER PIECE
Alternate	Hrs.	$					
Design							
Drafting			Original				
Eval.			Proposed				
Model Shop							
Pub'l.			FOR SUMMARY ONLY			BREAK-EVEN ANALYSIS	
Tech Lab			Recommended Proposal ___			Pres. vs. Prop. A ___	
Tooling			Dollar Savings per Unit ___			Pres. vs. Prop. B ___	
			% Savings per Unit ___			Pres. vs. Prop. C ___	
			Total Savings			Prop. A vs. Prop. B ___	
			(Based on Forecast) ___			Prop. A vs. Prop. C ___	
			Proposed Effectively			Prop. B vs. Prop. C ___	
TOTAL			Point ___				

Figure 9.2

EXECUTION PHASE

Date: ______________ Page ____ of ____

COMPARISON TO PRESENT METHOD

ALTERNATE ________

FUNCTION: ______________________ APPROACH: __________________________

ADVANTAGES	EFFECTED PARTS LIST (+) Add (-) Delete	RECURRING COSTS: LABOR & BURDEN	MATERIAL	TOTAL L-B-M	COST SOURCE
					DISADVANTAGES
TOTALS:					

NON-RECURRING COSTS

ALTERNATE	DESIGN		DRAFTING		EVAL.		TECH. LAB		MOD. SHOP		OTHER		PUB'L.		TOOLING		DOLLAR SUMMARY	
	HRS.	$	HRS.	$	HRS.	$	HRS	$	HRS.	$	HRS	$	HRS.	$	HRS	$	TOTAL	PER UNIT

Figure 9.3

VALUE ENGINEERING ANALYSIS

Page ____ of ____

ANALYSIS:	PROPOSAL NO.
SUBJECT:	

Figure 9.4

EXECUTION PHASES

TESTS AND EVALUATION: Detail the test procedure necessary to
verify that the function can still be performed and that quality,
maintainability, reliability, and systems compatibility have not
been sacrificed.

Figure 9.5

Chapter 10

THE PRESENTATION PHASE

The presentation phase can be considered an extension of the execution phase, where the detailed analysis and proposal recommendations were developed. It is often difficult to define where execution ends and presentation begins, because both share the principal objective (or function): to "sell the recommendations."

Some Value Engineers prefer to divide the presentation phase into two distinct sections. The first part, at the conclusion of the workshop, and the second, some two or three weeks later when the formal study document is completed. If a continuous five day seminar is planned, it may be advantageous to divide the presentation phase. The first part will be a milestone event in which potential conclusions, expectations, and issues are reported and discussed with the steering committee. Since an indepth analysis is difficult to accomplish within a one week VE workshop, the strategy is to "feel out" the steering committee members on open issues, gain concurrence with direction, and explore other concerns they may have. The VE team can then schedule the second part, or formal presentation, following the "clean up" of open issues, validating assumptions, and the publication of the study report. At the conclusion of part two of the presentation phase, the formal report would be distributed to the steering committee. There are a number of advantages to this split presentation approach:

1. The VE task team has an opportunity to test the acceptability of their recommendations and isolate those issues requiring resolution prior to formal presentation.

2. The steering committee becomes preconditioned to the recommendations which, if properly presented, raises their level of expectation. Members of the committee will begin to accept and commit to the proposal, making the formal presentation a closing rather that a selling event.

3. The quality of the recommendations, and the supporting documentation, will be greatly improved over the rush to complete by week's end.

Some Value Engineers find it equally beneficial to divide the seminar rather than the presentation; that is, conduct the information, speculation and planning phases in three days, then adjourn for two weeks, and reconvene with the execution and presentation phases on two subsequent days. During the two week break, options and approaches are investigated and analyzed in detail. When the team meets again for the execution phase, their level of technical confidence is increased which translates into a single, well developed report and presentation. Either approach is better than the more popular closing presentation at the end of the one week seminar.

Because it is difficult to separate the execution and presentation phases, this section will concentrate on the "stand up" or oral presentation, rather than on the written report.

Whether or not we like the term "sell" it is what we do most throughout our lives. Success is measured in terms of selling; in presenting suggestions, ideas, concepts, proposals, programs -- but most important, ourselves. Therefore, rule #1 in the VE presentation phase, as well as the real world, is: <u>To sell your proposal, you must first sell yourself</u>.

As the presenter of the task team begins the presentation, the committee members, representing the buyers, first evaluate the speaker. The result of that evaluation is as important as the validity of the proposal, because as it is being explained, it will either open or close the minds of the buyers to the proposal. This evaluation takes the form of three questions that the steering committee asks of themselves.

Evaluate the Presenter

> A. Does he/she understand the issues involved?
> B. Does he/she believe in the proposal?
> C. Is he/she committed to its success?

Let's discuss each question in turn.

A. Does he/she understand the issues involved?
To command the attention of the steering committee, you must first demonstrate that you understand the problem and how it affects <u>them</u>. The proposal you are about to present is a solution to that problem. If you can get the committee to nod their heads in agreement, by confirming that you understand and are addressing the <u>right</u> problem, you are off to a good start.

Second, there is no substitute for knowing the subject you are talking about. You do not have to be an expert in each phase of the study. If fact, credibility can be enhanced by calling upon a qualified team member to answer a question involving an "expert" opinion, rather than ducking or bluffing your way through an answer.

As spokesperson for the VE team, you should be knowledgeable in the following aspects of the proposal and team study.

1. The issues or problem
   How, why, when it developed; its impact on the individual committee people and the need for resolution..

2. The team's approach
   Defining of the problem, factors isolated and prioritized, alternates considered.

3. Proposals recommended
   The principal proposal and its back up alternates.

4. Expectations
   What will be the results of the study when implemented, both quantitatively and qualitatively.

5. Risks
   What are the known (risks) and what are the team's plans for managing them.

6. Investment/Payback
   How much will it cost in terms of time, funding, and people; and what is the investment payback.

Although the above topics are in a logical study order, the order of presentation is different (see "Organizing the Presentation").

B. Does he/she believe in the proposal?

1. Project enthusiasm
2. Understand the strengths and weaknesses
3. Be positive

Knowing the subject and believing in it are two different things.

Many presenters have stumbled through their presentations with "ers," "ahs," "ummm," and other nervous mannerisms but carried it off because they believed in the proposal, and that belief showed through. This doesn't mean that you have to be a "huckster," shouting through a megaphone. It does mean that you must be convinced and believe in the logic and resultant expectations of the proposal.

Comments such as:

"... I don't know why I was picked as presenter, I know nothing about..."
"... the team thinks it will work, but I don't know..." and
"... I would have approached the problem differently..."

tend to discredit the proposal regardless of its validity.

The key to resolving this question is "believability," for if you don't believe in the proposal, why should the people you are trying to sell?

C. Is he/she committed to its success?

1. Put yourself on the line.
2. Express a willingness to assist.
3. Go beyond the scope of your job.

Now that you understand the VE proposal and believe in it, are you willing to make it happen? This assumes that you can be assigned to the implementation of the proposal. Most managers know that if a person proposing an idea commits himself to the success of that proposal, the probability of achieving success rises significantly. Even if legitimate reasons prevent you from participating in the implementation of the proposal, an expression of honest desire to "... see the proposal through" would raise the confidence level of the committee. Some questions you can expect from the steering committee seeking that level of confidence are:

1. Have you considered...?
2. Do you honestly believe it will work?
3. Why did you select this approach?
4. What will you do in the event something goes wrong?
5. Where, in your opinion, is the weakest part of the proposal?
6. Do you have a fall-back position?
7. Did you plan for milestone reviews, and are they strategically placed?

A. The Oral Presentation

1. Rehearse your presentation
Rehearsals to your teammates will build confidence and improve the presentation. Your teammates, playing the role of the committee, will be tougher than the committee itself, because they know the questions to expose the weaknesses.

2. Talk to the audience
Do not prepare written speeches. No matter how well you may read, it will be interpreted as not knowing the subject. When you use charts or projected illustrations, face the audience and make eye contact. Address the managers most concerned with the particular issues you are discussing. The eyes of the audience will stay on you, rather than wander, if they know they may be the target of your eye contact.

3. Position yourself
Do not stand in front of the charts or visual aids, particularly when you are referring to them in your presentation. Call attention to the visual aids by stepping aside and pointing (with a pointer) to the areas you want to emphasize.

4. Distracting mannerisms
A pointer is an effective presentation tool, but it is very distracting when the speaker waves, or unconsciously plays with it. In the theater this is referred to as "upstaging yourself," because the audience is directed to the action of the pointer rather than the speaker. When you are through with the pointer, put it down. Pick it up again to make another point.

5. Project your voice
Speak clearly, at a normal conversational pace, and address the people furthest away from you. To project your ideas, you must project your voice.

6. Do not memorize
The danger in memorizing a presentation is in being distracted. Once that break occurs, it is almost impossible to recover without disrupting the logical flow of the presentation. Knowing your subject is the best defense against being thrown off the track.

7. Lighten the presentation when appropriate
Humor, in good taste, and applicable to the subject, is most welcome because it relaxes the audience. However, cynicism and profanity should never be used.

8. Repeat questions
Questions should be repeated before answering, for a number of reasons:
   a. It assures that the whole audience heard the question.
   b. It confirms that you understood the question.
   c. It gives you time to think and organize the answer.
   d. It avoids a two party debate (you and the questioner) which will cause you to lose control of the audience.

9. Show enthusiasm
This is in support of the second question, "Does he/she believe in the proposal?" A lack of enthusiasm can be interpreted as a lack of confidence in the proposal.

10. Be brief
The oral presentation should not take more than 20 minutes. This may seem difficult at first, but the time constraint will help sharpen the presentation.

Give the committee the pertinent facts and reduce to a minimum how you got there. The time constraint will force you to prioritize the issues. If the committee wants to hear more, they will ask you and the team to stay. Don't impose yourself on the committee with a long drawn out presentation.

B. Organizing the Presentation

Visual aids are helpful in organizing and selling the proposals. There is a variety of audio visual equipment and good instructions on creating effective visuals. The choice of equipment should be dictated by the resources on hand, complexity of the study, and the comfort of the presenter. Equally important is the organization and sequence of the presentation. Figures 10.1 through 10.8 illustrate a typical VE study presentation flow.

CHAPTER 10 QUESTIONS

1. True or False: selling yourself is the first necessary step to selling the VE proposal (explain).

2. True or False: delay the conclusions of the presentation for the end, to create suspense and hold the Steering Committee's attention (explain).

3. What are the responsibilities of the team's spokesperson?

VALUE ENGINEERING WORKSHOP

Project: _____

Team: _____

Logo

```
┌─────────────────────────────────┐
│                                 │
│                                 │
│                                 │
│                                 │
│                                 │
│                                 │
│                                 │
└─────────────────────────────────┘
```

TaskTeam

Division: _____   _____

Location: _____   _____

Date: _____ to _____   _____

_____

_____

_____

_____

_____

_____

The Introduction of the Study and theTeam to the Steering Committee

Figure 10.1

```
           OBJECTIVES                              RESULTS

    1. _____           1. _____
       _____              _____

       a. _____              a. _____

       b. _____              b. _____

       c. _____              c. _____


    2. _____           2. _____
       _____              _____

       a. _____              a. _____

       b. _____              b. _____


    3. _____           3. _____
       _____              _____

       a. _____              a. _____

       b. _____              b. _____




                        CONCLUSIONS

            _____
            _____
            _____
            _____
```

The Objectives, Results, and Conclusions
of the Proposal to be Presented

NOTE: To command the attention of the steering comittee, it is important
to bring the conclusion, or bottom line, up front, then explain how the team
got there. If you present the conclusions last, the audence may "run ahead"
in anticipation, and miss many key points.

Figure 10.2

APPROACH

Function _____

Proposal A _____

_____

Current	Proposed
(Sketch)	(Sketch)
$ _____	$ _____

Function _____

Proposal A _____ GFI _____

_____

Current	Proposed
(Sketch)	(Sketch)
$ _____	$ _____

GFI _____

Total Potential Savings

Other Benefits   a. _____

b. _____   _____

The Approach and Comparison of the Proposal
with the Current Conditions or Products

Figure 10.3

INVESTMENTS REQUIRED

$
_____   _____
_____   _____
_____   _____
                    _____

$ [   ]

RETURN ON INVESTMENT

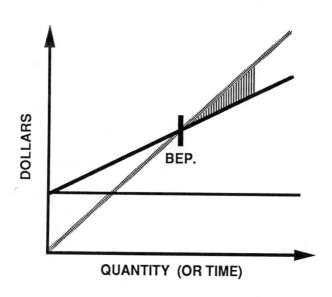

The Investment Required to Achieve the
Results and the Investment Payback

Figure 10.4

10-11

ALTERNATE APPROACHES

A. _____

    _____   (Sketch)

B. _____

    _____   (Sketch)

C. _____

    _____   (Sketch)

D. _____

    _____   (Sketch)

Other Ideas Considered and Their Disposition

Figure 10.5

RECOMMENDATIONS

Task   Responsible

A. _____   _____

   _____

   _____

   _____

B. _____   _____

   _____

   _____

   _____

C. _____   _____

   _____

   _____

   _____

D. _____   _____

   _____

   _____

   _____

Specific Recommendations Relating to the
Implementation of the Proposal

Figure 10.6

MILESTONE PLAN

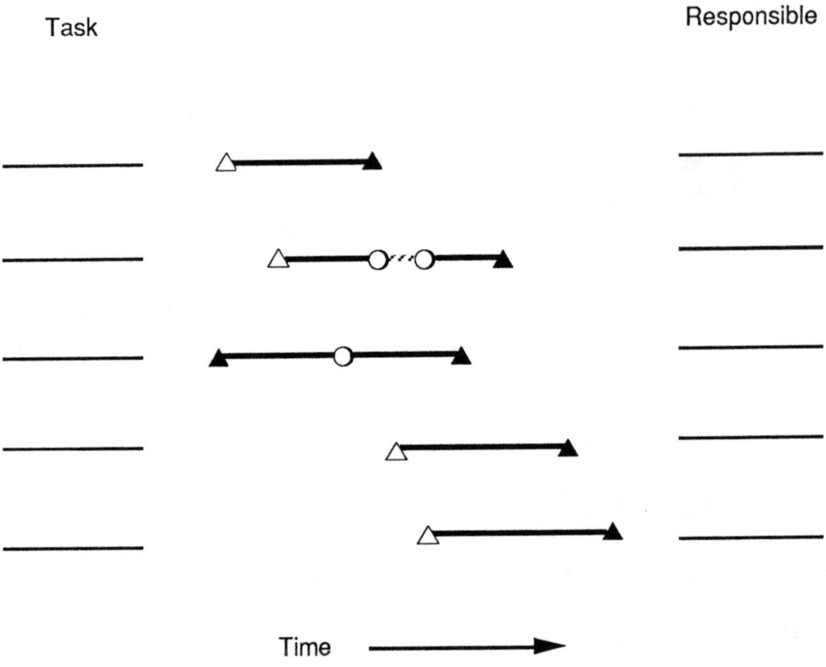

Task   Responsible

————   △————▲   ————

————   △———O⌒O———▲   ————

————   ▲———O———▲   ————

————   △————▲   ————

————   △————▲   ————

Time ————————▶

Notes ————————————————————————

A Milestone Plan Showing a Reasonable Time
From Start to Completion of Implementation

Critical decision points should also be noted indicating
"go - no go" conditions.

Figure 10.7

SUMMARY

A. _____

_____

B. _____

_____

C. _____

_____

D. _____

_____

A Short Summary of the Presentation
Emphasizing the Conclusions Once More

NOTE: It is important to leave the steering committee with action items and due dates before closing the meeting. This must be planned in advance. Someone must be responsible for follow-up actions. If this isn't resolved before the meeting breaks up, little if anything will be accomplished in implementing the proposal. Once the proposal has been "sold" and responsibilities assigned, the implementation phase can begin.

Figure 10.8

Chapter 11

THE IMPLEMENTATION PHASE

Excellent ideas are worthless if they do not incite positive action. Those actions, or "implementations" don't just happen. They must be planned and managed. Implementation is not normally included in the VE job plan (i.e. information, speculation, planning, execution, and presentation). One reason for omission is the Workshop Seminar, a popular format for performing Value Engineering. Following the completion of a one-week highly interactive workshop concluding with proposal recommendations, the participants return to their home departments. If the seminar was well planned, the task team members will participate in the implementation action. In any event, someone must be responsible and have the authority to initiate and manage the implementation of those proposals approved by management. Successful implementation of the Value Engineering proposal is the true measure of its effectiveness and must be considered as a critical part of the Value process. The implementation of a Value Engineering proposal closes the loop on the project and justifies the investment in Value Engineering.

Of those VE units that fail, most are caused by their inability to demonstrate tangible results in the form of resolving problems, capturing opportunities, and contributing to the accomplishment of goals in the business plan.

The approval of a Value Engineering proposal, even by an upper management level steering committee, does not assure that the proposal will be implemented. During the execution and presentation phases (Chapters 9 and 10), much emphasis was placed on "selling" the proposal. Once sold, it must now be delivered. That is the function of the implementation phase.

When does the implementation process start? Implementation is initiated at the very beginning, when the project is defined and selected for Value Engineering Analysis. During the project selection process, key issues should be resolved which impact directly on the probability of implementing the VE proposal after approval.

Key Implementation Issues
(Pre-Study Planning)

1. How is success to be defined and measured?
2. Are resources committed for implementation?
3. Is timing for implementation a high priority?
4. Which department will carry the major responsibility for implementation?
5. Is there a sponsor for the VE study project?

KEY IMPLEMENTATION ISSUES

1. How is success to be defined and measured?

Don't be trapped into thinking that cost reduction is the only measure of success. The real problem could involve sales, deliveries, distribution, customer services, etc. Product cost reduction may look attractive but it could be the wrong solution for the problem. A cost reduction action that reduces sales and profit is no solution.

2. Are resources committed for implementation?

Lack of resources is a major cause for no implementation action. The availability of resources in the form of funds and personnel assignment should be resolved before a VE study project is undertaken. If you wait until project approval to gain the necessary commitments, you will usually encounter resistance, because the actions required were not planned or included in the budget cycle.

3. Is timing for implementation a high priority?

If line actions are dependent upon the results and recommendations of a VE proposal, timing must be factored into the study and implementation schedule. Issues such as make or buy, new or modified products, capital investment or refurbishment, productivity improvement, etc., all have "opportunity windows." Failure to implement a VE proposal in a timely fashion could force a decision without the benefit of the Value improvement recommendations.

It would also be poor planning to change a design immediately after purchasing has committed the parts and material to produce that design or following new shop tooling and inventory buildup.

4. *Which department will carry the major responsibility for implementation actions?*

Each department operates under its own set of goals, objectives, plans and schedules. Unless the VE proposal supports those commitments, it will be difficult to get that department manager to accept new "imposed" assignments.

Changing the design of a product to improve its Value characteristics may seem worthwhile, but not necessarily to the design department. Design engineering may be busy with a new generation of products, and therefore, consider design modifications for cost or Value improvements a low priority. Advanced planning is necessary to schedule implementation actions with those departments affected prior to starting the VE study project.

5. *Is there a sponsor for he VE study project?*

Having a champion or sponsor who will endorse and "push" the VE proposal through implementation is good insurance. A champion may not be essential to the implementation process, but having a high level manager committed to the successful implementation of a VE proposal can clear away many roadblocks, authorize resources, and incite positive action. An astute Value Manager will try to develop such a champion during the early stages of project selection. Having a strong champion for a project should count heavily in the selection criteria for scheduling VE study projects.

The importance of a steering committee as an approval body was discussed in Chapter 10 (The Presentation Phase). However, the formation of a permanent steering committee, or Value Council, properly constituted, will have the authority to resolve the issues described above. In addition to its advisory functions, the steering committee acts as a single body in making upper management decisions necessary to institute, conduct and implement Value Engineering study projects (See Chapter 12).

Following the <u>approval of the VE proposal</u> and plan developed as part of the execution phase, a project manager should be assigned to manage the implementation process.

1. Assign a project manager.
2. Acquire operating funds.
3. Form an implementation staff.
4. Reconfirm milestone plan.
5. Develop and test model off line.
6. Report progress.

If the company has a VE department the project management function should be assigned to one of the VE staff members.

If the Value Manager is a one person facilitator/coordinator staff within the company, the Project Manager should be appointed from among the task team members. In any event, the assignment of a Project Manager is essential to the successful implementation of the Value proposal.

The first step taken by the Project Manager will be to confirm the project status and arrange for operating funds. This is accomplished through normal company channels. Some companies consider VE projects as overhead, in which the entire company shares in the expenses of implementation. Others view VE projects as a direct charge to the product line affected. In this case, a project authorization number is assigned and expenditures accumulated and reported against that project authorization. With the operating budget approved, the staff can now be assembled.

The implementation staff should consist of representatives from those departments directly involved in the responsible actions. Whenever possible, task team members should be on that staff, because they are most familiar with the intent, development, and expectations of the proposal and can resolve unforeseen issues arising during project activities.

During the execution phase, an event plan was developed identifying major milestones. These milestones are "go -- no go" gates designed to reduce investment risk. The plan also recommended the parallel development of one or two alternate approaches. The purpose of multiple development becomes evident if a problem is encountered that requires a major shift away from the primary approach. Such direction changes can be made without disrupting or requalifying the entire program.

In new product development or major redesigns, models should be built and tested "off line" or parallel to the production process flow.

The integration of changes into the production line should only occur when the VE proposals have been debugged and represent a minimal technical and financial risk of not meeting expectations. Once that stage is reached, the project can be handed off to the responsible departments, and the team members can return to their home departments with the provision that the team can be recalled if other problems occur. Progress reports should be presented to the steering committee at regularly scheduled meetings and when a major milestone is achieved. The committee, now the "investors," should be informed of the three "P's" -- progress, performance and prognosis of meeting the objectives of the project.

Guidelines for presenting progress reports to the steering committee are basically the same as those discussed in the presentation phase. However, some points to emphasize are as follows:

Progress Reporting

1. Submit agenda and documentation before the meeting.
2. Identify milestone completions and open issues.
3. Report expenditures against budget.
4. Present recommendations and corrective actions (if required).
5. Report probability of success and confidence level.
6. Open discussion.
7. Schedule next meeting.

A well planned and executed program also helps sell the concepts of Value Engineering through the steering committee. If the managers on the committee praise the performance of VE, its position in the organization becomes secured through the demand for its services.

Follow-up actions are necessary to validate the results of the VE project. Additionally, it represents an opportunity to publicize the project a second time. The most immediate follow-up action is to publicly recognize the participation of the team members and support services through memos, reports, and company newspapers. Certificates of achievement signed by the Chief Operating Officer and letters of appreciation will stimulate future VE task team participation.

At the appropriate time, a post audit should be conducted, validating the payback for the investment. That payback could be expressed in dollars, hours, manpower, sales, profit, etc. At this point it is important that the results are quantified. Intangible benefits will also occur, but their credibility will be lost unless backed by results that are measurable and supported by the finance department.

Follow Up Action

1. Recognize participants.
2. Publicize results.
3. Audit performance.
4. Close out project.

After a successful post audit, the study file can be logged and closed, and another VE project undertaken.

CHAPTER 11 QUESTIONS

1. True or False: Value Engineers should not take an active part in the implementation of approved VE proposals.

2. What are 4 key implementation issues to be considered in selecting a project for VE study?

3. Discuss the importance in VE of having a Steering Committee.

Chapter 12

MANAGING VALUE ENGINEERING

How to organize Value Engineering within a company depends largely on that company's size, product line, culture, and markets served. However, all VE units have common characteristics which impact their performance. The purpose of this section is to explore those issues and requirements that must be considered in the development of an effective, organizationally recognized Value Engineering unit.

First, we must assume that the company management in question desires to establish such a unit. This is a significant assumption, since it implies that the sponsor, or "champion," for VE has experienced or has heard of some impressive VE successes. It would be of value to the organizer of the VE unit to learn what success elements motivated the champion to sponsor VE. That information should serve to structure the goals and objectives of VE. However, let us begin with the most basic issues; the requirements for a Value Engineer.

THE VALUE ENGINEER: A PROFILE

The candidate must have a technical background matching the company's principal product, as well as the management and communication skills to address the broad range of disciplines that become involved in a typical VE study.

These attributes are necessary since his activity will take him through all aspects of the business in facilitating VE projects to determine the most effective, creative approaches. Since Value Engineering necessitates a substantial amount of direct communication, the candidate should possess objective and imaginative traits, along with diplomatic restraint but with a tenacious desire to accomplish the assignments. As a "full-time" Value Engineer, his work requires him to investigate, refine, and coordinate all VE proposals. He will uncover opportunities, evaluate approaches, organize task teams, prepare communications, publish, and submit the recommendations formally as an Engineering Proposal to proper authorities. He will then follow-up the project until final acceptance and implementation have been accomplished. The process of performing a Value Engineering study is graphically illustrated in Figure 12.1

Figure 12.1 summarizes the Value Engineering analysis to be performed regardless of the operating base of the Value Engineer. The characteristics of that organization can take on various forms.

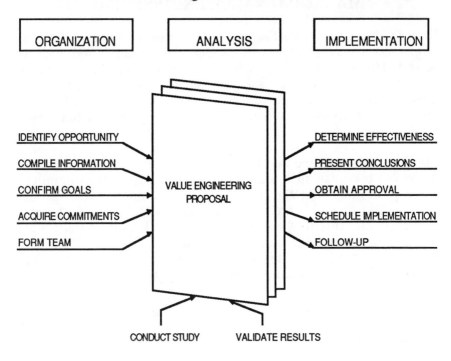

Figure 12.1

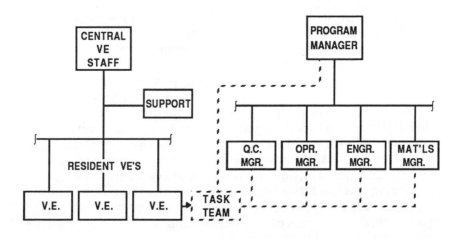

Figure 12.2

RESIDENT VALUE ENGINEER

The "resident" concept should be considered in a company organized into projects or programs. As the name implies, full-time, skilled Value Engineers are assigned from a VE central staff to "reside" on a project.

The Value Engineer reports to the project or program manager for day to day assignments, while administratively linked to a central VE staff (Figure 12.2). As a member of the program managers staff, the Value Engineer is dedicated to the success of that program, which is his principal responsibility. It is, therefore, important that staff and line VE performance goals not be in conflict. A popular means of financing VE activity is "zero balance" or to prorate the staff's operating expenses among the resident VE's. This would result in a number of positive features.

Resident VE Zero Balance Features

1. Prioritized staff and line goals.
2. Performance oriented staff.
3. Staffing related to company growth.

1. Prioritized staff and line goals.
Since the program(s) literally pay for the services of the resident Value Engineer, plus the prorated staff expenses, the program goals must take precedence over staff goals. This puts the staff in a program support mode, which is the proper orientation since it is the programs, not the central staff that generate profits. This approach also keeps the central staff "lean," since a high prorated expense could make the resident Value Engineer unaffordable. A disadvantage of this system is the VE staff may become too dependent on the program manager for support, tempting the program manager to use the Value Engineer for non-VE related assignments. If this becomes a common practice, VE could lose its identity, charter, and therefore, its reason for existence as an organized unit.

2. Performance oriented staff.
In a programs dominated company, it is the Program Manager that has the option of accepting or rejecting the services of a resident Value Engineer. Value Engineers will, therefore, gravitate toward opportunities that offer immediate, high yield results, which directly impact the program and benefit the Program Manager. The Program Manager's decision to utilize the services of a resident Value Engineer is very much dependent on the returns he can expect for his investment.

A major disadvantage is the inability of the VE staff to actively participate in long-term planning. Most program VE activities are a series of "fire drills" looking for short-term solutions. Long-term or strategic planning is rarely a priority issue at the program level, but it is on the executive staff level.

3. *Staffing related to company growth.*
Assuming a reasonable performance record, the growth of the VE staff is dependent on the number of program opportunities, and therefore, the growth of the company. Although this may appear beneficial and financially equitable to the company, one disadvantage of this system is the difficulty of assigning Value Engineers to evaluate the company's cost of doing business or the overall productivity of the company, unless overhead funding can be justified and authorized for such studies without penalty to the line or programs using Value Engineering services. A typical organization structure appears in Figure 12.2.

MODIFIED RESIDENT VALUE ENGINEER

A modified version of the program management concept, described above, is to assign and train a member of the program staff to act as the VE program representative, in addition to his normal responsibilities.

A major advantage would be in a smaller VE staff, not directly dependent on program funds for financial support. However, the lack of dedication, skill, and effectiveness should be carefully considered in opting for the lower funding advantages.

Companies organized around departments rather than programs could overcome the disadvantages of the modified resident VE concept because the department structure is more permanent than a program, and therefore, more in harmony with higher level, long-term company objectives. A departmental value program using the modified resident Value Engineer approach is shown in Figure 12.3.

DEPARTMENT VALUE PROGRAMS
RESIDENT V.E.'S

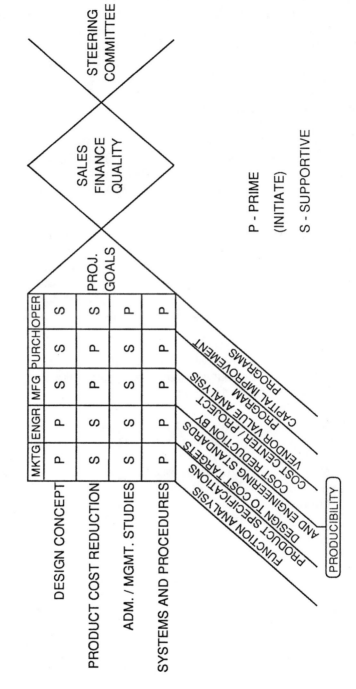

	MKTG	ENGR	MFG	PURCH	OPER
DESIGN CONCEPT	P	S	S	S	S
PRODUCT COST REDUCTION	S	P	S	P	S
ADM. / MGMT. STUDIES	S	S	S	S	P
SYSTEMS AND PROCEDURES	P	P	P	P	P

STEERING COMMITTEE

SALES
FINANCE
QUALITY

PROJ.
GOALS

P - PRIME
(INITIATE)

S - SUPPORTIVE

FUNCTION ANALYSIS
PRODUCT SPECIFICATIONS
DESIGN TO COST TARGETS
AND ENGINEERING STANDARDS
COST REDUCTION BY
VENDOR VALUE ANALYSIS
PRODUCT CENTER / PROJECT
CAPITAL IMPROVEMENT
PROGRAMS

PRODUCIBILITY

Figure 12.3

12-5

Each of the five departments shown in this example of a modified resident concept uses Value Engineering to achieve its departmental goals. However, the VE discipline is focused on the department's function. Marketing will find function analysis useful in defining new product specifications. Design engineering will relate to design to cost, Manufacturing to labor and material cost reduction, etc. Each department, can, therefore, establish its own VE goals and report on its performance.

When an opportunity arises requiring interdisciplinary task teams (i.e. design concept, product cost reduction, administrative/ management studies, or systems and procedures), residents can be formed into teams (or help form teams) to address opportunities.

CENTRAL VE STAFF

Since they are not line oriented, the company's central staff Value Engineers lack the opportunity to probe and uncover problems as efficiently as the previously described resident concepts. The central VE staff must rely on other departments for assignments and study recommendations to meet its objectives. Selected personnel are then organized into temporary VE project task teams financed by contributing departments. Most "one man" VE units operate in this manner. Many companies have one person Value Engineering units and boast of good performance records.

In terms of payback against vested VE expenses, the ratios can be impressive, but bottom line performance will be small. Another major disadvantage of this approach is that VE performance becomes dependent on the personality of the VE manager. Since there usually is no back-up support, the loss of that manager would result in the loss of the VE function. Bringing in a replacement from within the company or from the outside would almost require starting up the VE unit from scratch.

MULTI-FUNCTION VALUE PROGRAMS

A good combination of the various operating approaches thus far described is illustrated in Figure 12.4.

This approach distinguishes between the interdisciplinary task teams (Value Engineering), and departmentally assigned VE representatives (modified VE resident), and the central VE staff function (Value criteria) for skill improvement.

Value criteria cover the education, training, and associated activities, which include establishing and conducting Value Engineering training, orientation, and education programs. In addition, Value criteria creates, publishes and distributes bulletins, articles, papers, posters, progress reports and manuals, develops value measurement and performance techniques, and establishes professional position descriptions. In general, Value criteria is responsible for creating and auditing the professional standards of performance and for the overall value awareness in a company.

Value Criteria in any organization arrangement would be the function of a central VE staff unit. However, all functions could initially be handled by one full-time VE manager supported by assigned resident Value Engineers. As the activities grow, additional Value Engineers would supervise each of the three functions illustrated in Figure 12.4, thereby building up a VE department in proportion to the size of the company and the performance of the VE department.

NOTES

VALUE PROGRAMS

DIVISION PRES. OR V.P.
STEERING COMMITTEE
VALUE PROGRAM MANAGER

VALUE ENGINEERING PROGRAM TYPE	OPERATIONAL RESPONSIBILITY	DEFINITION	DURATION OF EFFORT	CHARACTERISTICS
VALUE ENGINEERING TASK TEAMS	VALUE ENGINEERING MANAGER	TASKS REQUIRING MULTIDISCIPLINE REPRESENTATIVES	ESTABLISHED BY STEERING COMMITTEE	GENERALLY UPSTREAM NEW PRODUCT DEVELOPMENT OR MAJOR SUBSYSTEM REDESIGN OF PRODUCT OR PRODUCT LINE / SOFTWARE STUDIES RELATED TO THE ANALYSIS OF SYSTEMS, PROCEDURES, OPERATIONS - NOT DIRECT PRODUCT RELATED
VALUE ENGINEERING RESIDENT PROJECTS	DEPARTMENT VALUE COORDINATOR	PROJECTS ESSENTIALLY WITHIN DEPARTMENTS RESPONSIBILITY	CONTINUOUS ONGOING EFFORT AS APPROVED BY DEPT. MGR.	GENERALLY DOWNSTREAM COST REDUCTION OF COMPONENT OR FUNCTIONS DIRECTLY AFFECTING COMPONENT AND PRODUCT COST
VALUE CRITERIA / TRAINING & EDUCATION	V.E. MANAGER	TRAINING FOR IMPROVING PROFESSIONAL SKILLS	TRAINING - AS REQUIRED EDUCATION - ONGOING	VALUE ENGINEERING SEMINARS USING 'LIVE' WORKSHOPS ON UPSTREAM OR DOWNSTREAM PROJECTS / EDUCATION MATERIAL PREPARED FOR UPDATING SKILLS

Figure 12.4

THE STEERING COMMITTEE

The steering committee, as previously discussed (see Chapter 11), is not only important in the implementation of a VE project, but mandatory for the support, planning, and development of Value Engineering within the company. Although the Value Engineering manager must administratively report to a single source, preferably the executive staff, his activities will cross most vertical lines of the organization. A steering committee, meeting periodically, will evaluate, guide, and identify priority opportunities for Value Engineering. Most importantly, they can back such guidance with the resources necessary to act.

TO WHOM SHOULD VE REPORT?

As indicated at the beginning of this chapter, the parental affiliation of the VE unit is dependent on a number of factors, including size, product, culture, and market. However, some general guidelines should be considered in selecting an organizational base for VE.

1. VE's reporting department should be a dominant factor in the company's principle business.

2. The department head to whom Value Engineering reports should have broad decision-making capabilities and be a willing supporter of VE.

3. That department head should also be as high as possible on the executive staff. Since Value managers have little authority beyond the administration of their own actions, the reflected authority of their direct report is key in guiding the attention of the line managers to the performance goals of Value Engineering.

There are many facets to developing an effective VE organization. If there is any single criterion that would spell the success or failure of Value Engineering within a company, it would be the VE manager's approach to his objectives.

To be successful, Value Engineering must become a resource to executive management in helping them solve problems and capture opportunities. If VE becomes self-serving, pursuing low level goals that do not support business commitments, it will become a low priority activity. Consequently, it will constantly seek management endorsements to survive and will be among the first to go during a business down turn.

THE VALUE ENGINEERING/ANALYSIS WORKSHOP SEMINAR

Overview

Value Engineering/Analysis training is conducted in the format of a workshop seminar. The workshop utilizes a "live" project that has been identified by management as needing value improvement. This format is used so the participants can get immediate feedback by applying the instructions directly to the project. Preparation prior to the workshop involves gathering information relative to the problem. The information is primarily market data to define the requirements.

At the conclusion of the workshop (generally five or six days), solutions or courses of action have been developed. The solutions or plans are documented in a presentation to the management decision makers. The presentation includes the proposed solution and the cost to implement the solution, the anticipated payback period, and an estimate of the time needed to develop, test, and implement the solution.

The management decision makers constitute a Steering Committee that will accept or reject the proposed program. The Steering Committee represents the managers of the major disciplines involved in the Value Engineering project.

The participants at a workshop seminar are highly qualified in their disciplines. From these trained participants, one is selected to be the Project Manager responsible for the subsequent implementation and follow-up. At the conclusion of the workshop, the other participants are available to assist as team members on subsequent studies or to conduct Value studies within their departments. Additional Value practitioners are trained either by working on a task team with others trained in the Value disciplines or through future workshop seminars.

The Workshop Seminar

The most effective method of teaching Value Engineering/Analysis is to learn the principles while applying them to a "live" problem or opportunity.

It could be argued that the techniques can be equally taught in a classroom situation, utilizing "canned" or textbook problems. This way there would be more control over the content of the course. Little pre-event preparation would be required; the course itself could be divided into smaller time units so the participant's time would not be so disrupted and the expense of the seminar would be minimal. The classroom students could be evaluated by testing their solutions to the fixed answers. Unfortunately, this approach leaves out one important aspect of Value Engineering/Analysis training.

In a classroom situation, the objective of the course is to acquire knowledge rather than proficient applications. In the "live" workshop, however, <u>the solution to the problem is equal in importance to the learning process</u>. Therefore, workshop participants learning the techniques must also possess the basic disciplines necessary to arrive at an acceptable solution. Relieved of academic pressure, the workshop team members have the creative freedom to explore the nature of the problem and propose approaches using the latest technology. Their test is the acceptance and successful implementation of their ideas and plans.

From an economic point of view, the initial cost of the workshop seminar is relatively high. However, it represents a good investment because the resultant solutions often yields a return significantly greater than the front-end cost and time spent in the seminar.

A typical seminar can be structured to accommodate from one to four teams of from five to eight members per team, each having a different problem or project. Larger single team seminars, with from twelve to twenty members, can be divided into smaller groups, addressing specific elements of the problem.

Since the Value discipline is applicable to a wide range of opportunities, each team could be assigned different and unrelated projects without conflict. With a few exceptions, the tutorial portion of the course is common to all projects selected. Its application to a given project, however, will require individual team guidance by the VE team leaders.

Selecting the Project
Criteria for selecting a project using the seminar approach in applying the Value disciplines should be as follows:

> The potential payback of the project.
> The priority or urgency of the results.
> Requirements for multi-disciplined inputs and dialogue.
> Requirement for participation from more than one location.
> The opportunity and need to train employees.

The project itself could be a hardware problem (technical or economic) or an opportunity; it could represent a new product entry or a product entry needing cost reduction; it could also be a "software" problem; the need to develop a procedure or a policy or to revise an organizational alignment; or it could deal with a market or business strategies.

The expectations of the project should be meaningful and representative of the objectives and investment in the Workshop Seminar.

Selecting the Participating Team Members
There are two significant points to consider in selecting the seminar participants. First, the problem or opportunity determines the talent mix needed for its resolution. Second, the selection of people to represent that talent and proficiency should be compatible with the results expected. If the problem involves market strategy and business planning, make sure the responsible marketing, engineering, and financial people are on the team. Likewise, a manufacturing problem should include the people who will be held accountable for making the ideas work.

The seminar will teach the participants the Value disciplines and techniques. It will demand and bring out the best in them. However, it will not increase their skills as engineers, manufacturing people, marketing managers, technical specialist, etc. They must have that talent prior to the seminar.

Pre-Event-Information Phase
Nothing is more detrimental to the successful completion of the seminar's objective than lack of information. Forty-five to fifty-five hours compressed in about a week is little enough time to learn the VE methodology. The case problem must also be resolved in that time period.

The task team participants should be notified about three weeks prior to the start of the seminar and provided with a list of information and data they are to bring with them. Identical letters should be addressed to all team members so that each participant can see the full scope of information required and the importance of bringing his portion of the data package.

It should also be emphasized that the participating team members will be responsible for implementing the approved recommendations, and in doing so, carrying the new found Value techniques into their own departments to teach others and apply the techniques to their daily tasks. As team members they cannot attend part-time. The team output is dependent on the collective contributions of each member of the team.

A typical list of information applicable to a hardware type project can be found in Chapter 2, "The Information Phase." The results expected, the project itself whether hardware or software, and the participating disciplines will determine additions, deletions, emphasis, and modifications to the list.

The Seminar Structure
As a means of directing full attention to the objectives of the seminar (training, problem-solving, and team-building), the seminar is structured to simulate those conditions designed to maximize the expected results.

Each team represents a new company, detached from its parent organization. The team members are, therefore, the "executives" or "partners" in this new venture, with the project representing that company's major product (or service). The name and logo of the newly formed company are decided by team members early in the seminar and the parent company becomes a prime "competitor."

The purpose of this simulation is twofold. First, it will discourage the emergence of the "they syndrome," that is, the conscious (or unconscious) desire to "please the boss" or to anticipate what the boss will accept or reject, rather than consider the problem in objective terms. Generally, the task team perceives its management as being very conservative. Management expects more unique solutions than task team members perceive. The management level, acting as the approval body or Steering Committee, looks for creative proposals because they understand that the seminar environment and structure encourages that line of pursuit. Also, looking at their parent company as a competitor encourages the team to expose weaknesses to more objective analysis.

Second, since the team must "sell" their proposal to a group of "investors" (represented by the Steering Committee), the proposal must cover the broad scope of the business impact as well as the technical solution to the problem. Strong team-building relationships develop as a result of the necessity to explore all facets of the problem. Each discipline feels the importance of its contribution in order to arrive at the best possible solution. The relationships formed during this seminar will have a lasting positive effect that goes beyond the tangible results of the Value Program.

Facilities
Ideally, the seminar should be located away from the office and the daily work routine. The intensity of the program requires that the team members be totally removed from outside distractions

throughout the working day, which could extend to 14 or 16 hours. The meeting room must be large enough to accommodate the participants comfortably as well as all the data and resource people called in to consult with the team. Equally important is adequate wall space, for all data will be presented on large sheets of paper that can be displayed and analyzed on the walls. The physical arrangement of tables and chairs should be suited to team participation and close-quarter communications. The facility should provide for lectures with full use of audio/visual training aids. When appropriate, "break-out" rooms for subtask team studies and discussions are advised. In determining the size of the room, consider the addition of the Steering Committee and their guests at the conclusion of the seminar.

Meal functions are an extension of the seminar. Breakfast is an individual preference. Lunches should be taken together, close to the meeting room (but not inside). A light lunch is preferred to a heavy lunch, which would be detrimental to the afternoon sessions. When evening sessions are planned, a one-half to one hour relaxation break period is recommended before dinner, with an organized dinner to follow.

It is important to keep the team together during these meal and break functions. Even if business is not discussed, the continuity of the team will be maintained as a functioning unit.

Controls
Control of the seminar is necessary to "pace" the program -- to allocate time for instruction and application and to allow the teams time to consolidate their approaches and present their recommendations. However, control must take the form of subtle guidance. The seminar leader cannot expect to develop and encourage an environment of creativity and freethinking on one hand, then contradict the approach on the other by demanding strict adherence to the conduct and schedule of the seminar. If the principle objective of the session is the solution of the problem, the agenda must yield to the expected results. If education and training have equal or higher priorities, the agenda should be less flexible.

Motivational Pressures
Motivational pressures to encourage full participation by all team members are encouraged. One approach is not to select the team spokesperson until the evening prior to the last day. The spokesperson is selected to organize and orally present the team's approach, analysis and recommendations to the steering committee at the conclusion of the seminar. As spokesperson, his presentation adds to the credibility and confidence of the recommendations

presented. Although complete participation by each member cannot be assured by adopting this approach, nonparticipation and complacency would be inevitable if the team's spokesperson were named too early in the seminar. The spokesperson chosen is also responsible for organizing the record of seminar activities and publishing the final report following the presentation to the Steering Committee.

Another motivational idea is to request steering committee members to "walk in" and make direct inquiries of their people regarding their approaches and progress. However, once the participants have been told to expect "unannounced" visits by higher management levels, these visits must be made. Failure of management to appear could imply a lack of interest on their part and will reflect in the performance of the team.

The Steering Committee
The steering committee consists of senior management personnel invited to act as a Review and Approval board at the closing presentations by the seminar task teams. This has a number of positive affects on the seminar personnel, as well as on the board. The presence of this steering committee implies more than passive interest. It represents active management participation in the seminar and its resultant recommendations. It is an opportunity for the task team to command the attention of the Approval Board Members at one time, on neutral grounds. Those on the steering committee who have not previously attended a workshop seminar will find the experience both rewarding and enlightening.

In the closing session, the task team will outline (in detail) practical approaches to the problems and specific recommendations for achieving project objectives. A renewed sense of motivation and team pride will be evident. The effects of the interdisciplined teams will be demonstrated in the depth of the analyses and variety of approaches considered in the proposals. Additionally, and perhaps most important, the team's commitment to making the proposed (and approved) solutions work will be apparent.

The presentation represents a milestone event: the completion of the workshop seminar. The team members are then allowed about one month (maximum six weeks) to test their assumptions, fine tune their data, and publish the final report. The Steering Committee is then reconvened for the closing presentation and approval of the recommended plans is requested.

The time period between seminar end and formal report allows the Steering Committee to question, raise issues, and reflect on the anticipated recommendations.

Implementation Phase

Implementation of the proposals generated by the workshop represents the most important phase of the program; the workshop objectives are not fulfilled until direct action concerning the disposition of the recommendations is taken. Regardless of the validity of the ideas presented and their potential results, the proposals are useless unless implemented.

Effective implementation requires more than an effort to obtain concurrences with the ideas presented in the workshop. It necessitates detailing the recommended approaches in a well-defined plan and documenting the rationale, assumptions, economic impact, and risk in all areas affected by the proposal's implementation.

To ensure effective management of implementation, responsibility should rest with the team member who has been assigned the presentation. He should be given the position and responsibility of Project Manager. Since the task team has developed the proposals after analyzing the alternate approaches and participating in the discussions and the development of conclusions, the team, led by the Project Manager, is in the best position to initiate the implementation phase.

This must be followed by tracking milestone events to verify the validity of the anticipated results of the proposal. The major implementation milestone events should be scheduled as report presentations to the Steering Committee, especially if the Steering Committee authorized implementation funds incrementally.

Count-Down Schedule

The events leading to the seminar begin after group management authorizes the project. The seminar leader or facilitator should allow a minimum of 30 days to prepare, coordinate, and make the necessary seminar arrangements. The following checklist is designed to assure that the seminar leader or facilitator is fully prepared for the session.

Four Weeks Before Seminar

1. Determine disciplines that will be utilized on the "live" workshop projects. Typically, each team should have representatives from:
   Engineering
   Market/Sales
   Manufacturing
   Purchasing
   Quality Control
   Finance
   Plant Management

2. Submit the team discipline make-up to Group Management with recommended personnel to fill those positions. Arrange a meeting with department managers to discuss participants, the nature of the seminar, the assigned project, results expected, training objectives, commitments, and support necessary.

3. Select and reserve facilities for the meeting. The facilities should be away from the normal working environment to avoid interruptions. These facilities can generally be obtained at a hotel, motel, lodge, club, college or community center. Facilities should have:

   _____ Sufficient room to permit each team to work at a separate table and to utilize flip chart easels. Minimum recommended room size is 20' x 20' for a single team (4-5 members); 30' x 30' for 2 to 3 teams.

   _____ Rostrum or equivalent for instructor

   _____ Easel and flip chart pad -- one for each team plus instructor

   _____ Overhead projector for transparencies

   _____ 16mm sound projector and projection screen

   _____ Videotape equipment

   _____ Provisions for coffee and rolls

   _____ Provisions for meals -- served in separate room or an area where participants can dine together

   _____ Computer with reflex or spread sheet and word processing software

4. Place request for copies of the training manual and audio/visual aids to Corporate Value Programs office.

Three Weeks Before Seminar

5. Finalize list of individuals to attend seminar.

6. Send list of participants to the Corporate Value Programs office

for preparation of certificates.

7. Determine others who might be invited to attend, such as:
   _____ Participants from other facilities
   _____ Vendors with applicable products to display to participants
   _____ Distributors, representatives and customers who might help define the requirements/problems involved
   _____ Representatives from regulatory agencies who might clarify requirements

   Contact identified guests for interest and availability.

8. Prepare rough draft of seminar agenda. Agenda should cover topic time, material needed, type of presentation, and presenter. The agenda should be distributed during the week preceding the seminar, preferably the last working day before the seminar.

9. Assign participants to teams. Equal distribution of skills among the teams should be assured.

10. Notify the Steering Committee of presentation date, place, and time.

Two Weeks Before the Seminar
11. Make arrangements for special speakers for the first day.
    _____ Keynote (should be a member of top management)

    Subject matter that should be covered:
        Objective of the seminar
        Support of Value Engineering
        Why these projects were selected
        Why these personnel were selected for the seminar
        Expectations from the seminar team(s)

    Market overview (from Marketing)
        History of product line
        Market growth -- quantity and customers
        Problem areas
        Target cost and market sensitivity

12. Notify participants by memo (see sample) of their selection for the seminar and furnish a list of data that they are to gather prior to the first meeting. See pre-event information phase.

One Week Before the Seminar
13. Issue training manual to participants with finalized schedule inserted (see attached model).

14. Check final arrangements. Verify that the items in item 3 are available.

15. Obtain materials for the participants:
    _____ Felt tip pens -- each team (red, black, blue, green)
    _____ Straight edge or yard stick -- each team
    _____ Masking tape -- each team
    _____ Sharpened pencils -- each participant
    _____ One large (3' x 5') poster board or other stiff cardboard -- each team

16. Make arrangements for speedy provision of typing, reproductions, illustrations, and viewgraphs. Resources at the plant should be available for quick response.

17. Prepare and arrange meeting room.

18. Arrange for photo coverage if desired.

19. Verify Steering Committee availability for team presentations.

CHAPTER 12 QUESTIONS

1. What are some of the advantages and disadvantages of a resident VE concept (line) vs. a central staff?

2. True or False: VE should always report to manufacturing because it is the biggest cost driver and the results are measurable (explain).

3. What are 2 major objectives of a VE Workshop Seminar?

**SUBJECT: V.E. SEMINAR PREPARATION --
(PROJECT NAME[S])**

Let me congratulate you on being selected by (GROUP PRESIDENT OR STRATEGIC BUSINESS UNIT HEAD) to participate in the Value Engineering Workshop Seminar to be held from (DATE) to (DATE) in (LOCATION).

A Value Engineering (workshop) Seminar is both a learning and a doing experience. As a team member, you will represent one of a number of disciplines, structured to apply the concepts of Value Engineering to a "live" situation. As such, there are two significant objectives of the Seminar:

> The output of proposed implementable ideas to effect nature and results expected of the projects.

> To learn the V.E. problem-solving techniques and apply them to your daily working environment.

To get the most out of the Seminar, the team will act as an independent company whose sole product line is the (PROJECT). The team members will represent the officers of the company, so that decisions, recommendations, and proposals remain within the team. This should not prevent you from seeking any "outside" specialty assistance to help resolve your problems.

On the last day, (DATE), the team will present its findings, recommendations, implementation plans, investments required, payback, etc., to a Steering Committee consisting of your Vice President, (NAME), and his staff. They will represent the investment board you are trying to "sell" to fund your program.

Although the situation is simulated, the actions are real. Each team member will, therefore, take an active and responsible part in implementing the proposals approved by the Steering Committee following the completion of the Value Engineering Seminar.

In preparation for the event, there are a number of things you should bring to the Seminar in the form of supporting data which will be combined with other team inputs and product information to make up the "information package." Your data input is important.

Combined with the other data of your team, it should represent a significant portion of the information needed to successfully achieve the assigned objective. As a minimum, the information you should be accumulating is as follows:

I. *Texts*
    Seminar texts will be furnished for distribution prior to the workshop. Please read the information and become familiar with the basic Value discipline. During the lecture portion of the workshop, supplementary data will be handed out to complete the workshop text.

II. *Schedule*
     All meetings (DATE[START TO END]) will be held at the (MEETING PLACE) in (CITY). All sessions will commence at your normal starting time, at the location designated. However, plan on evening sessions Tuesday, Wednesday and Thursday. A detailed schedule appears in the front of your text.

III. *Administrative Details*
     A. Dress is casual. No ties or jackets unless you feel uncomfortable *not* wearing a tie. Jeans and sport shirts are encouraged.

         The final day (Friday, DATE), the day of the Steering Committee presentation, you may want more appropriate dress, but this is your option.

     B. Meals: Arrangements will be made for all lunches, coffee, sweet rolls, and refreshments.

         When we work late during the week, arrangements will be made with the facility to serve dinner to the participating teams.

     C. There will be an "Attitude Adjustment" hour at 5:00 each evening (except for Friday) to relax and gather a "second wind" before continuing.

     D. Calls: Incoming calls will be restricted to Seminar business and emergencies only, so make arrangements to break away from your normal work routine.

I am sure you will find the Value Seminar experience rewarding from a personal point of view. Although the work won't be academically difficult, you will find exercising your creative abilities mentally exhausting at times, so bring with you your most positive "up-beat" attitude.

If you have any questions or problems relative to the Seminar, please call me at (PHONE NUMBER).

(YOUR NAME)
(TITLE)

JJK/ngp
Enclosures

VALUE PROGRAM WORKSHOP
SEMINAR OUTLINE

SESSION _I_ DAY Monday

LOCATION: _____

DIVISION: _____

PROJECT: _____

DATE: _____ TO _____

NO. OF DAYS: _5_ HOURS: _40+_

| TIME | | ELAPSED TIME | | SUBJECT | | NOTES |
FROM	TO	HOURS	MIN.	TOPIC	ACTIVITY	
8:00	8:15	--	15		Introductions	Value Manager
8:15	8:45	--	30	Remarks	Keynote (kick-off), where we are now, problem discussion expectations	V.P. - G.M.
8:45	9:00	--	15	Remarks	Administrative Details -- Anouncements	Value Manager
9:00	10:00	1	--	Lecture	The Value Concept -- An Organized Discipline	DTC/Cost Reduction
10:00	10:15	--	15		COFFEE BREAK	
10:15	11:00	--	45	Film	"Value Analysis"	Discussion
11:00	12:00	1	--	Lecture	A V.E. Workshop in Miniature (A Canned Example)	Project: Staple Remover
12:00	1:00	1	--		LUNCH	
1:00	2:30	1	30	Lecture	A V.E. Workshop in Miniature (Continued)	Exercise
2:30	3:30	1	--	Lecture and Discussion	THE INFORMATION PHASE -- Data Gathering and Problem Identification -- Function Determination	Problem: "Who's Got The Zebra?"
3:30	5:00	1	3-	Project	Review Information and Discuss	Each Team Member to Present His Input
5:00	6:00	1	--	Attitude Adjustment	Continue Team Discussion of Data	

NOTE: This schedule is a guide only, subject to change by the needs of the project

12-23

VALUE PROGRAM WORKSHOP
SEMINAR OUTLINE

SESSION II DAY Tuesday

LOCATION: _____

| TIME | | | | SUBJECT | | NOTES |
| FROM | TO | ELAPSED TIME | | TOPIC | ACTIVITY | |
		HOURS	MIN.			
8:00	9:30	1	30	Lecture and Project	Function Evaluation Techniques (Random Function Determination, Numerical Evaluation, FAST) Function Analysis System Technique (FAST)	Identify Project Components/Function/Cost
9:30	10:00	--	30	Film	"Function Cost Worth"	Refer to Information Checklist
10:00	10:15	--	15		COFFEE BREAK	
10:15	12:00	1	45	Project	Develop FAST Model, Structured by System, Assign Target Costs	Arrange for Drawing Model
12:00	1:00	1	--		LUNCH	
1:00	3:00	2	--	Project	Develop FAST Model, Structured by System, Assign Target Costs	Test FAST Model
3:00	4:00	1	--	Lecture and Exercise	THE SPECULATIVE PHASE -- Creativity, Traits and Techniques	Refer to Speculation Checklist
4:00	5:00	1	--	Lecture and Project	Brainstorming -- Alternative Solutions	Roadblocks, Penalties and Booklet
5:00	5:30	--	30	Attitude Adjustments		
5:30	OPEN			Project	Complete FAST Model (If Required)	
					NOTE: This schedule is a guide only, subject to change by the needs of the project	

SESSION III DAY Wednesday
LOCATION: _____

DIVISION: _____
PROJECT: _____
DATE: _____ TO _____
NO. OF DAYS: _____ 5 HOURS: 40+

VALUE PROGRAM WORKSHOP
SEMINAR OUTLINE

| TIME | | ELAPSED TIME | | SUBJECT | | NOTES |
FROM	TO	HOURS	MIN.	TOPIC	ACTIVITY	
8:00	8:30	--	30	Lecture	Film "Why Man Creates"	
8:30	10:00	1	30	Project	Review Status Brainstorming (Group Ideas)	
10:00	10:15	--	15		COFFEE BREAK	
10:15	12:00	1	45	Information and Discussion	Open for Vendor or other consultant Presentations	Guest
12:00	1:00	1	--		LUNCH	
1:00	2:30	1	30	Lecture and Project	THE PLANNING PHASE -- Evaluation of The "Gut Feel Index" (GFI)	
2:30	5:00	2	30	Lecture and Project	Development of Concepts and Evaluate Alternatives	
5:00	5:30	--	30	Attitude Adjustment		
5:30	OPEN			Project	Continue Alternate Evaluation -- Recap Progress to Date, Assess remaining time frame against open task	
					NOTE: This schedule is a guide only, subject to change by the needs of the project	

VALUE PROGRAM WORKSHOP
SEMINAR OUTLINE

SESSION IV DAY Thursday

LOCATION: _____

DIVISION: _____

PROJECT: _____

DATE: _____ TO _____

NO. OF DAYS: 5 HOURS: 40+

TIME				SUBJECT		NOTES
FROM	TO	ELAPSED TIME		TOPIC	ACTIVITY	
		HOURS	MIN.			
8:00	9:00	1	--	Project	Complete Alternative Evaluation	
9:00	10:00	1	--	Lecture	THE EXECUTION PHASE -- Mechanics of Analysis, Break Even Point, Pareto's Theory of Maldistribution, Support Data	
10:00	10:15	--	15		COFFEE BREAK	
10:15	12:00	1	45	Project	THE EXECUTION PHASE (Continued) -- Assess Economic and Technical Benefits/Risk	
12:00	1:00	1	--		LUNCH	
1:00	1:30	--	30	Lecture	THE REPORT PHASE -- Content and Arrangement -- Selling Proposal	Refer to Supplementary Information
1:30	5:00	3	30	Project	Draft Report, Graphic Arts	Task Team Presenter Selected
5:00	5:30	--	30	Attitude Adjustments		
5:30	OPEN				Project "Catch-up" and Complete Strategy	
					NOTE: This schedule is a guide only, subject to change by the needs of the project	

12-26

SESSION V DAY Friday

LOCATION: _____

DIVISION: _____

PROJECT: _____

DATE: _____ TO _____

NO. OF DAYS: __ HOURS: 40+

VALUE PROGRAM WORKSHOP
SEMINAR OUTLINE

| TIME | | ELAPSED TIME | | SUBJECT | | |
FROM	TO	HOURS	MIN.	TOPIC	ACTIVITY	NOTES
8:00	10:00	1	--	Project	Clean-up Proposal Details	Detail Implementation Requirements, and Major Milestone Events
10:00	10:15	--	15		COFFEE BREAK	
10:15	12:00	1	45	Project	Dry Run Team Presentation and Critique (Identify Post Seminar Assignments)	Select Date for Final (Published) Presentation
12:00	1:00	1	--		LUNCH	
1:00	2:00	1	--	Project	Finalize Presentation	Task Teams
2:00	3:00	1	--	Project	Team Presentation to Division Management Steering Committee and Guests, Comments and Questions	Task Teams
3:00	3:30	--	30	Discussion	Group Management -- Closing Comments	V.P. -- G.M. Steering Committee
3:30	4:00	--	30		Wrap-up Seminar	

NOTE: This schedule is a guide only, subject to change by the needs of the project

VALUE PROGRAM WORKSHOP
SEMINAR OUTLINE

SESSION ___ DAY ___
LOCATION: ___

DIVISION: ___
PROJECT: ___
DATE: ___ TO ___
NO. OF DAYS: 5 HOURS: 40+

TIME		ELAPSED TIME		SUBJECT		NOTES
FROM	TO	HOURS	MIN.	TOPIC	ACTIVITY	

12-28

APPENDIX

CHAPTER 1 ANSWERS

1. The customer, user, or buyer

2. Esteem, Exchange, and Utility; or Want, Worth, and Need

3. VE looks for the best function/cost balance. This could result in a cost increase, but by enhancing wanted functions, sales and profitibility would be improved.

CHAPTER 2 ANSWERS

1. Pre-event is the gathering of information relative to the project. Post-event is sorting, classifying and structuring the information in a usable format for analysis.

2. Basic functions describes the principle reason for the product or service. Secondary functions describe the design or approach used in carrying out the basic function(s).

3. By using an active verb and a measurable noun.

CHAPTER 3 ANSWERS

1. An activity describes the method selected to perform the function of group of functions, similar to a secondary function. A function is an end or purpose that an activity is intended to perform.

2. How →, Why ←, When ↕

3. The Scope Lines define the area under study and identify the Basic Function(s).

CHAPTER 4 ANSWERS

1. Problem sensitivity, fluency, flexibility, and originality

2. A negative response to an idea. A discouraging opinion lacking creditability.

3. Suspend judgement. The wilder the idea, the better. Quantity of ideas wanted over quality. Combine and build upon ideas.

CHAPTER 5 ANSWERS

1. SJ, SP, NF, NT

2. Myers-Briggs Personality Indicator (MBTI) describes basic styles of behavior.

3. MBTI Analysis can assist in forming a balanced personality team, with high creativity attributes.

CHAPTER 6 ANSWERS

1. Analytical or evaluation.

2. To screen and rank ideas by selectively applying applicable requirements and valid constraints.

3. False

CHAPTER 7 ANSWERS

1. Amortized value of $P = \dfrac{NR}{Q} + R$.
   Fixed value of $P = NR + R(Q)$.

2. No

3. For 3 proposals, 3 BEP's, for 4 proposals, BEP's.

CHAPTER 8 ANSWERS

(See problem examples at the end of the chapter.)

CHAPTER 9 ANSWERS

1. To create, validate and "test" proposals in response to VE Project assignments.

2. False

3. False

CHAPTER 10 ANSWERS

1. True

2. False

3. To organize, manage and present the results of the VE Task Team to the Steering Committee.

CHAPTER 11 ANSWERS

1. False

2. Can success be defined and measured? Are resources available for implementation? Is the assigned project a high priority issue? Which department will carry the major responsibility for implementation? Does the project hav a champion or sponsor?

3. •Represents the approval body
   •Guides direction of VE to mainstream business
   •Authorizes necessary resources
   •Judges the contributions of VE

CHAPTER 12 ANSWERS

1.

ADVANTAGES	DISADVANTAGES
•Dedicated to program success	•Focus on short term solutions
•Program funded	•No support for company issues
•VE growth linked to program	•Loss of assignment control

2. False

3. Traning and problem resolution

ENDNOTES

1. Kaufman, J.J. "Understanding the Problem Before You Work the Solution." In 1983 Society of American Value Engineers Conference Proceedings.

2. Parnes, S.J. "Do You Really Understand Brainstorming?" In *A Sourcebook for Creative Thinking*, edited by S. J. Parnes and H.F. Hardin, New York: Scribner, 1962.

3. Gamarra, M.T. *Erroneous Predictions and Negative Comments Concerning Exploration, Territorial Expansion, Scientific and Technological Development, Selected Statements,* Library of Congress Legislative Reference Services, Washington, D.C. 1969.